THE BAREFOOT
PRINCESS

ISBN 978 -2-940412-09-9

PRINCESS ZAHIA

In collaboration with
Monique Tissot

THE BAREFOOT PRINCESS

D.P.PLANETE

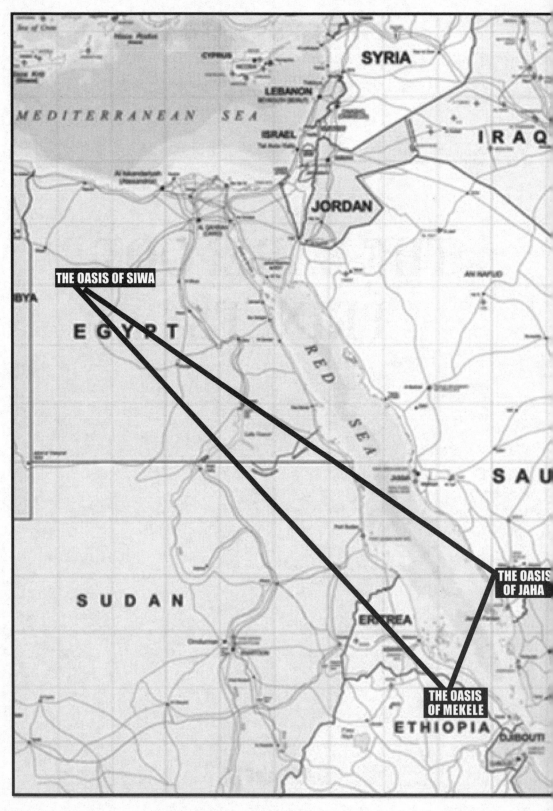

Preface

THE ANGEL OF MERCY

I met Zahia for the first time in 1994, in Rwanda, during the Hundred Days War.

At the time I was editor of the magazine "Terres d'Histoire", and I had not gone to Africa to cover the genocide in which 800,000 Tutsis were massacred by the Hutus in power, but to meet the team of Bare-foot Doctors, whose original action in the field is a model for others.

Contrary to other humanitarian missions, these doctors immerse themselves in the local culture and relieve misery and suffering with the means at their disposal in the country.

Dr Jean-Pierre Willem - the pioneer of this human adventure - told me, "It is useless to bring our Western medicine with its side effects to these people, poles apart from their mode of life. We provide them with the facilities of current research to identify and make use of the action of indigenous medicinal plants.

"We work alongside local healers, herbalists and shamans, and this mutual exchange of knowledge and respect is both effective and beneficial for them as well as for us."

While I was talking to him I noticed an exceptionally beautiful woman working in the midst of the wounded and dying. The copper sheen of her skin and her proud bearing made me think she was Indian, but I learnt that she was in fact Ethiopian, a race descended from the Queen of Sheba and King Solomon, which explained her fine Semitic features.

With infinite grace and compassion, the young woman went from one to the other, distributing comforting gestures and gentle words to those who suffered. She seemed an angel of mercy in the midst of all this distress.

Zahia was using a balm that she took carefully with the tips of her fingers from a shell that recalled one of those conch shells that children hold to their ear to hear the sound of the waves.

With infinite delicacy she spread it on wounds caused by bullets and machetes, and victims who had been moaning in pain seemed immediately soothed.

I asked Dr Willem if it was a powerful analgesic, like morphine perhaps...

"No", he replied, "It's a balm made from plants that Zahia prepared herself, as her grand-mother taught her."

"Aren't you afraid it will make things worse?"

The Angel of mercy

"They have nothing more to lose. We have tried everything, without success, to save their limbs from the gangrene that is destroying them, and this woman alone has worked miracles. You know, our science has its limits, and Zahia has powers which are beyond us."

The following day I learnt that the condition of a young soldier whose leg had been treated by the healer had improved. The wound had become healthy and there was no longer any question of amputation.

From that moment I watched Zahia's movements from a distance, careful not to frighten this reserved young woman, so devoted to her task.

Each of her gestures seemed part of a ritual, a harmonious dance to charm the spirits.

On several occasions I heard her chanting a strange music which resembled an incantation, and saw her carefully placing a little pearly shell on the wounds, which immediately caused the patient to fall into a deep sleep.

Zahia only stopped when she reached the limit of exhaustion. Sometimes she even missed meals, which were the only real opportunities to relax during the long days.

One evening I met the young woman in the shower block, and was able to admire her magnificent hair which, freed from her headscarf, fell rippling and brilliant down her back. I decided to approach her and introduce myself to her.

"I'm a French journalist, and I should like to ask you a few questions."

She agreed gracefully, in perfect lilting French. She spoke fluent French.

The barefoot princess

"Were you born here?"

"No", she told me, "I come from Ethiopia, but I have lived for years in an oasis in Saudi Arabia."

Gradually I overcame her reticence. Little by little, without ever giving me the names of places or persons, this very secret woman revealed snatches of her story.

I learnt that she had been taken from her family when she was eleven and sold to the owners of an Egyptian stud farm.

I wanted to know more, for quite clearly Zahia was a cultivated young woman who spoke several languages and had nothing of the slave-girl about her. Her fine, long hands were not those of a worker accustomed to difficult tasks; on the contrary, she had the elegant, soft hands of women of quality who have only known needlework and the art of the caress.

"Yes", she admitted to me one evening, "I was fortunate to be able to escape from my terrible condition, thanks to a chance meeting. Today I am wealthy, respected and happy, but the trials I have suffered remain forever fixed in my memory. That is why I have a duty to relieve those who suffer. My childhood prepared me for this task, for through my grandmother and a long line of healers, I have acquired special knowledge which I have to offer to the most vulnerable."

Then I questioned her about her miraculous balsam:

"Why not give the secret to the Bare-foot Doctors who spend their time treating suffering people? You cannot be everywhere at once, Zahia, but they can. It would certainly be a precious help for them."

The Angel of mercy

"That is true", she replied, "But the herbs I use for my balm cannot be found everywhere, and anyway, on its own this balm can only give passing relief. The gift is in my hands, and unfortunately I can only pass it on to my own descendants..."

At this point I recalled something said to me by Dr Rolande Maffre, a Parisian acupuncturist, who wished to meet one of my friends who was a magnetic healer.

"My knowledge of acupuncture is not sufficient to explain that some of my colleagues who use the same points and the same meridians do not obtain the same results.

I have learnt that behind the needles there is the human element, and some hands enter into osmosis with them to increase the therapeutic effect. That is why to understand this phenomenon I need to talk to empiric healers, because knowledge is not enough ...."

"But Zahia, this is a gift from heaven, and it belongs to everybody ..."

"Yes, I know", replied the young woman, "But despite my willingness to share it with others, it is impossible. That is why I work in the field whenever I can. It is unjust, but that is how it is. I can share my knowledge of herbs, but the spirits respond to me alone."

It took me more than a month in daily contact with Zahia, before I dared ask her to allow me to write a book about her unusual life and her experience as a shaman.

The barefoot princess

"I don't think so", she said, "It wouldn't be right. There are so many people still living that I love and respect, and I wouldn't wish to hurt them or do them harm."

"But we can change the names of people and places, Zahia. You tell me that today nobody knows your face, so your true identity will remain hidden ..."

After a moment's silence, during which I expected the worse, her soft, sensual voice murmured:

"So it will not be an interview, or a biography? If you promise me that, I will accept your offer willingly."

Faced with that reply, which seemed like a ray of sunlight to me, I thanked her profusely and added:

"Agreed, Zahia, we will call it a "roman vérité" and I promise you that you may confide in me with no fear of being uncovered."

So every evening after a day caring for the wounded and consoling the dying, Zahia devoted some of her time to recounting her story to me.

A factual story, but behind it questions linger: good, evil, the visible and the invisible, and dualities like love and hate.

So day after day, I recorded her words on my tape recorder, but to my great regret my mission came to an end and I had to return to Paris, without completing the recording of the beautiful Ethiopian's secrets.

The Angel of mercy

We promised to meet again, but more than twelve years passed before our next meeting. Twelve long years to discover the end of a story which, incredible and magical though it is, is nonetheless true.

During that time I received a few postcards from the world's flash points, and they all ended with a "See you soon!" which raised my hopes, but Zahia never gave me her address, so I could never reply.

Then we met in Kenya, as if we had only said goodbye the day before. And the game of confidences started again, with a background of other horrors, other sufferings that Zahia had tried to relieve with the same courage and the same fierce determination.

This "roman vérité" is the simple transcript of the incredible story of Zahia, slave princess and shaman. And I can assure you that although I helped to set the hundreds of pages that I received like so many raw diamonds, the words you are going to read were born in the very heart of Zahia.

A heart that beats henceforth only for others and for her Prince!

Monique TISSOT

Foreword

MESSAGE OF HOPE

I hesitated for a long time before agreeing to the publication of my story. The twelve year interruption in my confidences to Monique Tissot is due to a series of distressing events - the two year war between Ethiopia and Eritrea which caused more than 80,000 deaths or the great drought in 2000 which killed more than 100,000 of my people - but to be perfectly honest I must admit that there is the shadow of a missed opportunity in this respite.

My first reservation came from the fear of hurting those I love, but it was not the only one. The proposal to give my biography a romanticized form reassured me about that. Yes, I have changed names of people and places, but although I have voluntarily confused the trail, my story is nonetheless authentic.

Makele, the Siwa oasis, the kingdom of Jahal and Grimaud are real, but they are not necessarily the exact places where I lived through my childhood, my enslavement and my rebirth.

The barefoot princess

I should simply like to avoid the places where my spirit was forged, these crucibles of my personal alchemy, being one day pointed out like the famous château d'If, where tourists visit the cell of an Edmond Dantés who only existed in the imagination of Alexandre Dumas. It is because my story is true that I want to avoid those that I love being the object of misplaced curiosity.

Today, these seven years of life, which turned a wild child into the woman I desired to be, have the value of a quest for me. I have found my personal legend: this book must help you to find your own.

I do not seek fame. I wish to remain that woman of the shadows who - as my grandmother once did for me - shows you that any road, however arduous, can lead you one day to enter into the light, or more modestly, to become "better". This is the target I have given myself.

My story is like something out of a novel, but it is true. Perhaps people who are unable to read behind the words will class it in the much-maligned category of airport novels. Too bad for them, or for me, if I have been unable to transmit the fundamentals to them.

Inspiring people to dream is a marvelous act in itself, and as you do, I love to be carried away by great adventures and fine love stories. However, it is not enough for me to rely only on emotion. I have a message of hope to share with you.

I am neither a writer nor a philosopher, but in this book I wanted to deal with themes which are dear to me, themes which concern the universal. That is not easy when courage is one's only talent!

Message of hope

On thinking about it - I've had plenty of time for that! - it seems to me that some people, some situations which have marked my life, can find an echo in each of you.

You don't have to have undergone the same trials: the interior adventure is so much more inspiring.

What is important is to understand that a great pain can give birth to hope. That the separation does not prevent the soul from blossoming again.

I would like all those who have been deprived of their land by misery, famine or a natural catastrophe, to understand that they only have to let go in order to make this absolute evil the soil of their rebirth.

I am talking about those children who are uprooted and sold to rich families who use them as slaves, which unfortunately still happens today.

I wish to make people understand that adopting deprived third world children - however some may consider it to be a good gesture - can cause incredible suffering. Do people realize what heartbreak these children feel? What wounds bleed forever in their hearts?

It is because I have lived through that, and succeeded in healing from it, that I have the right and the duty to speak about it.

No, I am not ashamed to say that I sometimes went hungry. That my naked feet were often cut. That the fire of the sickle burnt my hands. And yet..... I had a happy childhood.

With us, the solidarity and spirit of the tribe were always present, and the little orphans found their place and the love they needed, without any need to steal their roots to do so.

The games I will tell you about will perhaps seem trivial, but make no mistake, the wheel of a bicycle can make the spirit travel as well as a Barbie doll. A simple marble can create as much wonder as a hugely expensive gift.

It was not destitution that tore my heart out: it was being exiled. And I think of all those who are faced with that separation, that wrench that lacerates one's flesh and wounds the spirit, who will perhaps understand me and say to themselves that all is perhaps not lost.

The law of return exists: I am the living proof. Sometimes it is enough to believe it to pick up the threads of a broken destiny.

I should also like those who suffer from the weight of traditions and religions to understand that this is not a fatality, that sometimes it suffices to free oneself from it to become a free man or woman.

The fact that I was not excised - and I lived it as a shame - nearly made me miss out on love. Today I know that it would have been worse to miss out on pleasure....

My grandmother understood that before me: she was able to transgress the taboos and avoid me suffering that ritual mutilation that would have made me frigid, frustrated, and afflicted with irreversible psychological wounds. Thank you once again, Mamina...

These ancestral rites from another age led me to ask myself questions about the foundations which unite men and women in the name of love.

I would like to say to all those who have been the victims of a sexist education, that love is not slavery but the communion of two spirits who vibrate in unison.

It is impossible to love lastingly if one is not yet mature. That our own way is still at the early stage. True union cannot be born from a lack - what we modestly call complementarity is that of two fulfilled beings. Twin flames from which alone can be born the spark of life which ties us to the divine.

And then there is the magic which even today makes my soul tremble. The magic of an old lady who is no longer with us but whose every word and every gesture still makes my memory sing.

I'm sure that one day you too have met somebody like my Mamina. A unique being, full of love and commonsense, who taught you to look at the world through different eyes.

You mother, who knew how to calm your tears or your little hurts with a loving kiss.

A grandfather perhaps, who took you to collect mushrooms for the first time, and taught you to love the warm damp atmosphere of autumn woods.

A country quack who relieved your sores or calmed a burn because he knew how to ward off fire.

Or even the family doctor who not only healed your body, but cared for your spirit, simply by listening to you.

The barefoot princess

Take a good look, my friends, there is no shortage of exceptional men and women in this world.

All you have to do is open your ears and your hearts to drink from the spring of their wisdom.

You have certainly met proud and spirited beings, who have suffered, sometimes taking the wrong road, but who were able to communicate their humanity and their passion to you. .

For me it was horses, but for you perhaps it was photography, the theatre or music...

There is magic everywhere: in a child's smile, in the breath of the wind on the plain, in the wash of the sea or the movement of a field of wheat.

It cares nothing for man's beliefs. It has neither god nor master. It knows that in each religion, prayer or invocation, only love counts, only love transcends everyday life.

I have communicated with the spirits of plants, stones and animals. But I have also drawn the means to raise my soul ever higher from the eye of Christ or in the prayers of the Prophet.

I have experienced shamanic rituals with the same intensity as animist ceremonies.

Heaven is too vast to have only one messenger, and every act of faith helps us to surpass ourselves.

Today I am over forty, and I could add many more chapters to this book, recounting my personal experiences as a woman.

Message of hope

However, what is essential is the period of seven years that allowed me to attain my dream. The rest would just be literature.

I matured very quickly, possibly because I had been prepared for it from an early age by my grandmother's initiation. Perhaps yours is beginning today, whatever your own age may be. Awakening knows no clock and the heavens may open the route to you at any moment.

At this stage in my life, Buddhist philosophy appeals to me. I had the good fortune to meet an exceptional person, the Dalai Lama, and his teaching, his art of happiness, seem to me to be the culmination of everything I have loved in my heart, my spirit and in my flesh. But for you, believer or not, everything can begin tomorrow...

The key words of my story are hope, love and tolerance, and more than my adventures, which I hope will interest you, that is what I should like to share with you.

ZAHIA

*It is only with the heart that one can see clearly;
what is essential is invisible to the eye.*

Saint Exupéry : The Little Prince

1

THE SPIRIT TREE

"Zahia...Zahia... Where are you? Come back!"

No! I don't want them to find me. I don't want them to take me! I don't want the black man to snatch me from my land like a weed.

And so I run. I run. Faster than my name. Faster than the tom-tom that beats in my heart like the death bell in the old church.

I trip on a root. My knees are bleeding. My feet are burning from the heat of the earth, the earth ruined by sun and salt.

Where can I hide in this plain that stretches as far as the horizon? As far as I can breathe.

"Oh Mamina why have you abandoned me? Where are you now? Please answer me, I beg you.....

Tell me where I can find shelter and escape from these men who are after my life?…

The barefoot princess

"The spirit tree: do you remember, little girl? It will protect you and give you the answers you are waiting for."

"The spirit tree! Oh thank you, Mamina. I didn't think of it. It is so old and shriveled that I thought the terrible onslaughts of the simoon had killed it....Our tree, Mamina, what a good idea!"

"Don't lose any time! Run, little one!"

"But where can I find you, Mamina? I miss you so. I need you, I need you near me. You are so good at warding off the demons of fear."

"I am in the murmur of the breeze, in the reflection of water on the salt lake, in the cold light of the stars, in the waving of the grasses on the savanna. And above all, I am in your heart, little one, because it warms my soul and protects me from oblivion."

I rise to my feet and run. Again. With all my strength. With all my eleven-year old legs. The cries are getting closer:

"Zahia! Zahia! Where are you? Come back!"

The hunting pack is coming closer.... But I am not afraid. The spirit of my grandmother has spoken - I am no longer alone, I am not crying.... or is the wind drying my tears? I feel nothing any more, I run like an automaton.....

Finally, I can see my tree in the distance. Yes, the tree, our tree, is still there. Growing in the midst of nowhere. Its leafless arms beseech the sky. Its twisted roots spring from the bowels of the earth, as if it wished to flee to somewhere less arid. Under the dried scales of its powerful trunk the sap flows and exhausts itself to give it, still, the appearance of life.

The spirit tree

"This baobab is a master-tree", Mamina used to tell me, "One of the last of its race."

At its feet, after walking for several days, we used to come and place cowry shells, collected from the banks of the salt lake. And then the ritual began....

On each shell, you traced a sign that only you knew. With inward-looking eyes, facing the spirits that dwelt in your soul, you chanted strange songs coming from the depths of time.

And then the tree replied. Its branches trembled. Its scales gave out cracking sounds that underlined your chant. Its roots became animated by voluptuous spasms, and I was the wondering witness to an enchanted love display.

When you recovered your spirits, you asked me to choose the finest of the shells, the one whose mother-of-pearl heart shone like the sun, and you said:

"Little one, climb quickly into the hiding hole, my old legs no longer have the strength, and deposit this cowry in the heart of the tree so that it can absorb its Force, and to thank it. With its help, from tomorrow we will be able cure those who suffer and read the future to give new courage to those who have lost hope."

Of course Mamina, the hiding place: that is where I will take refuge. They won't find me, and will give up hunting me like a desert gazelle...

With my trembling legs and bruised feet I have difficulty climbing into the hollow of the tree more than six feet above the ground, but I finally reach it, and there I see the little pile made by the hundreds of cowry shells that generations of my ancestors have left here.

25

The barefoot princess

I slide in by the side, but to do so I have to huddle up, for the hiding place is narrow, and I have grown a lot since our last visit.

There I feel protected, nestled like a baby in its mother's womb. Above the recess, the tree spreads out to the summit.

"That's where the spirits live, little one. You only have to open your ears and they will give you their messages."

To avoid hearing the calls of my pursuers, ever more insistent, I close my eyes and caress the cowry you left me, Mamina, on your last bed of suffering.

"Each time you touch it, little one, the gift will live in you and you will be able to speak to the other worlds, just as I can, and our ancestors who passed it on to me."

My body trembles back and forth, and the song of the spirits bursts from my lips. My sight reels, and I no longer see with my bodily eyes, but with those of my spirit....

Soon a fluid being forms above me in the narrow chimney of the tree. I hold my breath, so as not to disturb the awaking presence.

The luminous spirit takes form, comes to life, and becomes a woman.

The woman is strikingly beautiful, dressed in an iridescent tunic, and wears an emerald necklace whose green light envelopes me like a silk cloak. Her expression shows infinite compassion and tenderness.

The spirit tree

"Listen, little girl, and open your heart. I have come to tell you that it is useless to try to escape your destiny, for the great misfortune to come will give rise to an immense happiness that will dispel your pain for ever."

"Lady of light, don't you know that my mother has sold me as a servant? That the black man has come to take me away, far from my family? And even worse, all those I love are looking for me? Isn't it a cruel fate for a little girl to be betrayed by her own people?"

"Yes, I know all that, Zahia, but you must look beyond the mirror of appearances. Your mother thinks that this will spare you from the miserable lot that burdens her since the loss of your father.

And she is also very afraid for you, because you have discovered the place where the pitiless arms dealers hide their guns. They are looking for you, and what they have in mind for you is far worse than what is waiting for you in Egypt.

You think you are not loved, but the opposite is true. Your mother is afraid for your life, and you must not hold it against her for giving a few pennies to the village children to encourage them to find you: she is sure it is for your own good."

"But this land is my land, and it breaks my heart to leave it. When I touch the cowry that my grandmother left me, all I can see in life is sadness and desolation. Who are you to tell me that a perfect happiness will grow from all this misfortune?"

"Look at me, Zahia. Do I look sad? Poor? Desperate? No indeed! And this is who I am, little one: I am You ... in seven years...

The barefoot princess

I am Princess Zahia: she who loves and is loved. She who relieves the misery of the world. She who can read in the hearts of men....

I do not have the right to tell you more, but I hope this vision of your destiny will help you to come through the difficult years.

You now know that each suffering, each injustice, is only a step towards a glorious future. Let go, little girl, and all will be well ... I promise you."

The return to my body is very hard. It terrifies me to leave the celestial vision to return to my mortal body, exhausted by my flight, my panic and the cold. I tremble all over and I discover and incredible sensation that was unknown to me: the deafening sound of my heart resounding in my head. I really feel I am about to explode.

The sun is going down and the shadows are full of hostile presences. The calls are now so close.... it is only a matter of minutes before I will be discovered.

Suddenly, a face appears on the edge of my hiding place: it is Lila, my best friend, to whom I confide all my secrets - even that of the master-tree. Alas!

"I've found her"! she calls to my assailants.

"Come now, Zahia, you know that we don't mean you any harm. On the contrary, each of us would like to be in your place.

The family you are going to is rich and powerful. You will be able to eat all you want. Wear real dresses, and perhaps, even ... wear shoes!"...

The spirit tree

Before I have time to reply two muscular arms, those of Elias, the village smith, drag me from my hiding place. .

"Elias, only a few days ago I healed the terrible burn that made you suffer a thousand deaths: why do you too have to betray me ?!"

Hurt, powerless, given up to the enemy by those I hold dear, I fall to the ground and roll into a ball to escape the looks that pierce me from all sides.

I want to disappear. Take root. Find you in your earthly clothing, sweet Mamina.

Why don't they understand that I would prefer to be dead rather than leave all that is dear to me, part of me?

Why don't they know that I would suffer less from falling into the hands of gun-runners than those of the people I love and are accomplices in my betrayal?

There are a dozen of them in a circle around me, I don't need to look up, I can feel them as a she-wolf feels the presence of human predators : by their smell.

There is Daimon, the shepherd, whose leg I saved when he got caught in a fox trap.

Selma, the healer, to whom I gave the precious recipe for my grandmother's balm.

Rassim whom I cured of a nasty cough that tore his throat and chest.

Fatima, whom I delivered of her child who refused to be born in the normal way.

The barefoot princess

And all the others, my friends, my brothers, to whom I revealed the secrets of their souls and their futures.

Don't they know that I am the last of my line and they are going to lose their future shaman as well as their friend?

Disturbed by the words of the Lady of light, I don't know, I no longer know, if these familiar faces are rejecting me or if they love me so much that they are depriving themselves of my help to ensure what they believe will be my happiness.

Just behind them, my mother is waiting, frozen to the spot. Her eyes are full of tears, but all I see in my distress is the pocket of her blue apron, filled by the money given her by the black man.

"How are you, Zahia", she says to me, "You gave us such a fright?"

I try to reply, to express my pain and my anger, but nothing comes from my lips. I remain speechless....

Grief has not only torn my heart. It has also taken my tongue. I have become dumb.

In a fog, I hear Elias say to Selma:

"We'll have to chop down this tree: it's dead."

And Selma, pointing to a green bud which has just grown on the branch which touches the hiding place, replies:

"You're wrong, Elias, this tree is still alive, look, the child's tears have revived it ..."

The spirit tree

Lila supports me on the way back to the house where the man in his dark suit with his cursed money is waiting for me. He looks at me with a glimmer of pity and says:

"Why have the masters chosen this little child, she is sickly and unruly: she will never be able to take on the work they plan for her .... but orders are orders!"

Tonight, I will not sleep at home. My small bundle is already in the boot of the long black car.

The driver is getting impatient and the door of the limousine bangs on me with a dry noise like that of a coffin that is being shut. A black night that is burying my childhood for ever.....

Only the desert can cure despair:
There you may weep without fear of making the river overflow.

Ahmadou Kourouma.

2

PRISONER OF THE DESERT

I have absolutely no recollection of my journey and my arrival in Egypt. I know only that as soon as the car drew away from my people, I was seized with terrible convulsions. My body braced itself, arched, became rigid, and with all my being, refused the separation.

The black man bent over me, and held me down on the bench seat with his powerful arms. He stared at me with his one cruel hawk-like eye, and forced a bitter-tasting drink between my closed lips, which instantly provoked an immense black hole.

When my eyes reopened the sun was high in the sky. We had left the evening before as night was falling.

"We will soon be there", said my jailer.

They were the first words he had spoken in my own language, and already he seemed a little less frightening.

But there was nothing reassuring about the black eye-patch which covered his dead eye, the terrible scar across his jaw and his sober gandura, like Father Gilles' robe when he conducted burial ceremonies.

The barefoot princess

My head still groggy, I glanced through the lowered window. The view was appalling. I had imagined that this exile would take me to a town in the heart of Egypt, where I could find a way to escape. Friends, allies, people of my own race perhaps, who would help me to return to my family.

But stretching in front of me to the horizon was the desert. Immaculate dunes. Cliffs sculpted by the desert wind. An endless defile of jagged, menacing rocks.

The track became bumpy and the driver was obliged to stop several times to remove heavy rocks which had fallen from the hilly slopes. .

Suddenly a violent wind rose, slapping our faces. The black man quickly wound up the window. Immense dust devils rose up, obscuring the sky. The storm buried us, like a shroud, and night replaced day. Even the powerful lights of the limousine could not pierce the tornado of grey sand.

The car came to a halt but, unlike me, the men did not seem worried.

"Don't be afraid, kid, it will soon be over!"

I didn't believe it, but a few minutes later the desert had gotten its colors back and the sun was blazing again. But I had not found hope: it was impossible to escape from here.

It was possible to slip past the men's guard, but there was no way to deceive this hostile and baleful environment.

Prisoner of the desert

So I made myself very small, and dug myself into the brown leather cushions, as though I could be swallowed up in them. The animal smell comforted me a little, it reminded me of the smell of the zebra I had tamed, who ate *tef* seeds from my hand. I dosed off.

"Wake up, kid, we're here".

Shaken by the firm hand of the black man, I couldn't refrain from admiration at what I saw.

An ochre-colored palace suddenly appeared in an ocean of palm trees, surrounded by gushing springs. Swathed in a spectral blue, its crenellated towers defied the sky, making it look like a fortress.

"We are here, Zahia. This is the oasis of Siwa, where you are going to live."

Supported by the steward - I was still very weak - I entered a huge room, which despite the suffocating heat outside, was icy cold, and found myself facing the people who were going to become my masters.

The black man abandoned me. Alone and afraid. Suddenly I missed his presence.

An imposing man stared at me, frowning under his thick black eyebrows. His piercing eyes undressed me, like a filly in the livestock market. I even expected him to force my mouth open to look at my teeth, as horse dealers do.

Over his white djellaba the master wore an impressive curved knife whose sharp blade had certainly cut off hands before, and perhaps even....heads.

The barefoot princess

The woman with him wore a long brocaded dress covered with multicolored veils. Her hair was plaited and adorned with colored pearls, such as we would wear in my tribe for feast days, but hers were precious stones, not painted wood.

However, it was her straw-colored hair that fascinated me most, and her face, as pale as cotton flowers: it was the first time I had met a white person, and I learnt later that she was English.

The couple spoke a language I did not know, with harsh accents. Arab, perhaps. I could understand nothing of what they were saying, but I could understand the expressions on their faces: indignation, disdain, mockery. They laughed as they looked at me, as though I were one of the baboons who live on my savanna.

Admittedly I was in a pitiful state. I had not been able to wash after running away. My dress was in shreds; my legs were scratched by the grass, and as I ran I had lost the scarf Mamina had given me that usually covered my hair. It was uncombed, tousled, and fell on my shoulders in a tangle like a serpents' nest. I looked like a wild child, or one of those beggars who ask for charity outside churches.

At a sign from the couple, a servant girl came up to me. She was about 15 and wore her hair in the style of my tribe: the koun'a. Her hair was tied at the top of her head and fell freely down her neck. That told me that she was an Ethiopian from the Tigre region, as I was. This at least was lucky, because in my country there are more than 80 different dialects.

Prisoner of the desert

"Ethiopia is the Tower of Babel", Mamina used to say!

The young girl had also understood that we were from the same region: she addressed me in our tongue,

"My name is Chavha. I've been in Egypt for five years, and I work in the kitchens. The Master has told me to be your guide."

Chavha was obviously waiting for me to reply, so I showed her I had understood what she said by pointing to my left and right ears with my index finger, then I drew a cross on my lips with my finger, shaking my head to say no, to show her that I was dumb.

With little gestures and signs I also showed her that I wanted to know what the masters were saying. Why did they seem so irate? Why did they laugh at me?

Chavha hesitated a moment, so as not to hurt my feelings no doubt, then she said,

"They think that Father Gilles, who made you come here, is raving mad. You are much too young, far too thin and above all.... you are frightfully dirty."

Then, as if with regret, she translated the rest of their conversation:

"There is no question of having that slattern serving people, but she will be alright for the animals ..."

"That's why they have ordered me to take you to the sheep barn to replace Akar, who has just broken his leg. Come along, I'll settle you in, and show you your tasks".

The barefoot princess

I followed Chavha, who carried my bundle and a red blanket like those that the Red Cross gave us when there were floods. On the way I grabbed a stick and drew my name in the sand: *Zahia*.

Being called *"little one"* didn't bother me, but in my heart it was reserved for you, Mamina. Even if one day I became somebody of importance, as the Lady of the light had predicted, I will always be your little one.

Chavha led me to a foul-smelling, windowless storeroom, separated from the sheep by no more than a thin partition. Despite their nearness, I could feel that the unhealthy room was full of presences.

"Akar lived here for over 10 years," said Chavha," and he managed to give this place a little of his spirit".

Strange ornaments cut from newspaper decorated the walls. Silver paper stars made a halo around an image of Christ which had mostly lost its colors. There were even shells incrusted in the walls that reminded me of my dear cowries.

From the ceiling hung a dozen plaited straps holding gourds, no doubt used for drawing water from the river.

However modest this little room might be, it was now my home. Nobody would take the risk of affronting the smell, and as for the spirits, well, they have no nostrils!

My only concern was the probable return of Akar. His leg would heal, and I couldn't see myself sharing this hovel with him.

Chavha, who was obviously gifted with great intuition, could feel my anxiety.

"Don't worry, Zahia, Akar won't come back. As soon as he is back on his feet he has decided to go back to his father in Cairo. He wants to study to become a priest."

Now I understood better the magic which emanated from the place. Even if I was closer to the animist beliefs of Mamina than those of Akar and his Christ, faith and prayer awaken walls in the same way, when the heart is love.

Yes, here I was at home, I could lick my wounds and who knows, as the Lady of light had said, see them heal one day....

On the beaten earth floor, two bails of straw formed a bed where henceforth I would be able to dream of my family and friends. Chavha dropped my blanket and my small baggage on it.

The sheep barn was immense, with more than one hundred sheep bleating pitifully. The straw was wet and ill-smelling.

"For two days nobody has taken care, changed their bedding or fed and watered them," Chavha told me.

That upset me terribly. Animals are my friends and their distress was a cruel echo of mine.

"That's your job now, Zahia, you have to change their straw every day, feed them and water them. But

39

you also have to take care of the ponies, in the stables next door. Polish their saddles and the boots of the master's children, so that everything is always ready when they wish to go for a ride."

"And what about meals?" Timidly, I pointed to my mouth. I had eaten nothing at all since my attempted escape, and hunger was gnawing at my stomach.

"Over there, in the buildings you can see in the distance, you can eat with the servants and grooms every morning, midday and evening."

Grooms! The word rung in my head like a call. As well as the ponies, were there also some of those superb pure blood Arab horses that I had so admired when my father took me and my sisters to the horse fair that was held twice a year in Gondar? I sketched a horse with my hands. Chavha understood...

"Oh yes, Zahia, here in Siwa, the master raises the finest race of horses in the world: Egyptian pure blood Arabs. There are more than 200 of them frolicking around the oasis. The desert princes and emirs compete for them. They come to this breeding farm, which is highly renowned, to choose them and buy them, to make them the most precious gems of their kingdoms."

Then she added, with the same firmness as my mother when she wanted to warn us of a danger:

"You must never go near their pens or their stables, Zahia, because only Dagmar and those who serve him have that privilege. Don't forget, because you life is at stake. Dagmar is pitiless. He whips to death anyone who so much as looks at his horses."

Prisoner of the desert

After that terrible warning, Chavha said to me:

"There are also wash-basins, toilets and showers over there, and you look as though you could use them ...."

I signed to her that the buildings were a long way off, especially at night...

"Well, you'll just have to manage, kid. To wash, there is the sheep's trough, and you'll find a patch of straw for the rest.... the sheep won't mind and as it's you who does the cleaning ... what does it matter!"

Then the young girl showed me the shed where the pitch-forks and animal fodder was kept, and the large bin where I should throw the dirty straw that the tractor came to collect each morning. The bin was so high that I couldn't even reach it with my hand.

"Of course, Akar is at least two heads higher than you ... but there are wooden crates, and all you need do is pile them up until you are at the right height."

I was already imagining myself climbing the crates with each forkful of straw, and began to panic: I didn't know if I would have the strength to do it.

"I'll come and collect you later for lunch, Zahia, but right now I have to leave you, because if I'm not on time to prepare the meals they beat me.

The mistress brought a special whip from her country - she calls it a cat of nine tails - each strap has knots that tear your flesh. I've felt it once, because I dropped a plate, and I had to stay in bed for several days.

Look, I still have the marks."

The young girl pulled up her dress and showed me her raw scars - yet the punishment was meted out two weeks before!

I promised myself that if I could find the plants that go into Mamina's miraculous balm, I would treat her terrible scars.

The pain must have been particularly intense, because the whip had cut into her ritual scarifications, a garland of purple flowers sculpted in to the skin of her back.

In my heart I thanked Mamina who had been able to convince my parents to spare me from such mutilations.

"She is from a line of shamans", she said, with her natural authority which tolerated no contradiction, "Her body must remain as Nature made it, otherwise, she will never become the temple of the spirits."

"You had better do your work well," continued Chavha before slipping away, "You are so skinny you will never survive such a punishment".

I didn't have the time to bemoan my fate, nor that of my new friend, because I had to look after the sheep as soon as possible.

Before, however, I took the time to undo my bundle: I needed to change, and I was curious to know what my mother had prepared for me.

I emptied it onto my straw mattress and found a tunic, creased but clean. I pulled it on, after cleaning myself quickly in the sheep trough: I had neither soap nor towel, so I rubbed myself down with the blanket. It would be dry by evening.

It made me itch and my skin was red, but as my mother used to say when she rubbed me down with her loofa after bathing me in the river:

"It's good for you : it helps the circulation! "

I looked at the rest of my things spread out on my bed. The inventory was quickly done: my flowered Sunday dress, some underwear and a mysterious cardboard box.

Inanimate objects: do you have a soul?

Alfred de Musset

3

THE BOX OF TREASURES

When I opened the mysterious box, I was overcome with emotion and tears filled my eyes, but they were tears of joy.

It contained all my personal treasures, and awakened all my memories, like sap-filled buds.

I took them out one by one, felt them, held them close to me, and scenes from my happy past passed rapidly through my mind, turning this place of exile into the most beautiful bedroom in the world.

A marble rolled into my hand, and all the memories of my savanna came back to me...

I saw myself again at six years old, walking on the long track leading to school. It was my first day at school, just after the *tef* harvest. I still had blisters on my hands from the scythe.

"That's the way to learn, my girl!"

The barefoot princess

I was happy to see my friends again. Our huts were too far from each other and I only saw them once a week, for Mass. Because we were too young to do penitence, we weren't allowed to take part, so we waited for our parents in the church garden. Only my mother, who was very pious, took part in the service. Coptic Christianity didn't interest my father, and I never adopted it myself.

"I am a descendent of King Solomon and one of his servants," he used to say, "And even if I don't practice Judaism, it would be an offense to my ancestors to pray to a false messiah".

As for Mamina, since the day when Father Gilles surprised her near the spirit tree and called her a stregha (which means a witch), she refused to have anything to do with him.

"I prefer the company of spirits," she would say, "Rather than that fiend of God, who only preaches intolerance."

"Mamina, if you knew that this same priest persuaded Mother to sell me, you would be angry for ever!"

I was always on my grandmother's side, but I used to go with Mother because it was the only day when I could meet children of my age.

School frightened me a little of course, but I was overjoyed at the thought of being able to share the laughter and games of the other kids every day.

The first day at school was difficult for everybody. The teacher only spoke the official language, Amharic and we couldn't understand a word of what she said.

The box of treasures

It was such a relief when the bell rang for the lunch break! Each of us opened his own basket, but looked secretly to see what those of the others held.

Ayrad, who already had the soul of a little chief, decided that it would be fairer to put everything into a common bowl and share out. So we laid down leaves of ensete (a sort of banana tree) and spread out the food our mothers had prepared for us.

Injera pancakes made from teff pastry were used for plates. Each of us filled them either with mashed vegetables, or pieces of lamb or chicken cooked in yoghurt and spices. There were dates, guavas, and fresh fruit juice. A real feast! When we had devoured everything, including our plates, we still had an hour's playtime in front of us.

Dyna had brought a bicycle wheel, which she had found in a trash heap, and she taught us how to play with it like a hoop, by pushing it with a stick. But the game didn't really interest the boys.

Adal took a little bag from his pocket, out of which rolled multicolored balls, like dolls' eyes.

"These are marbles," he said, "My father brought them back yesterday from Harar. We'll make a racetrack on the ground, and whoever is first at the finishing line with his marble will have the right to keep it."

I applied myself very seriously to the art of pitching marbles, but the others were more skilled, and soon passed me. I was very disappointed, because I so wanted to win that precious marble with its agate colors.

The barefoot princess

Adal noticed my disappointment. Beneath his tough appearance he was very sensitive, and at ten years old, he was much bigger than me.

"Here," he said, taking me aside, "This marble is for you".

"But I didn't win, in fact I was last ... Why?"

"Because you're pretty, and this marble is the color of your eyes. Don't tell the others or they'll poke fun at me!"

Dear Adal, your glistening marble has never left me, and that evening, despite my loneliness, just holding it in the palm of my hand gave me back my smile. It was a smile with a salty taste, as my tears ran down into the corners of my mouth, but it seemed like the taste of my salt lake in the happy days when I bathed there with Mamina. I missed it all so much!

❖ ❖ ❖

The second treasure I drew from the magic box was a silver Coptic cross. I was given it the day I was baptized, with the ritual drop of wine which is placed on the baby's lips, and replaces holy water in my country.

I had removed it from my neck only three years before, when Mamina had given me her magic cowry and her powers. I know that my choice caused a lot of pain to my Mother, for she had so hoped that I wouldn't follow in the steps of my grandmother.

Dearest Mother.... I wasn't going to wear your mateb, but I decided to hang it on the wall next to the image of Christ that Akar had left me.

The box of treasures

That divinity - messiah or not - would not anger the spirits. They are drawn only by the beauty of souls, and this Christ had light in his eyes. After all, heaven is vast enough to have several messengers!

"The only thing that oppresses me, Mamina, when I think about religion, is that matter of the showers."

"Why concern yourself with such trivial details, child, when you have just spoken like a true shaman?"

"Yes, I know, Mamina, but that worries me nevertheless. You see, Chavha told me that the women's showers are not individual, and the servants wash themselves naked. How can I hide ... my difference?

I can't find the proper words to express my shame, Mamina, but I am whole ... intimately. When I was changing my little sisters' diapers that I realized that I'm not like them."

"That was my decision, child, I tricked the matron by telling her that I had excised you myself, but it's not true.

You see, my love, I didn't want them to hurt you. I suffered too much myself.

You will understand when you get married, Zahia. And if your husband is not a lout, he will be happy and proud to share that pleasure which is the salt of life with you."

"I don't really understand what you mean, dear Mamina, but for the moment what worries me is the way other people look at me."

The barefoot princess

"You have no need to feel shame, child. It's those who dare to do that to women that should feel embarrassed. But if it still bothers you, bathe in the river, or use the sheep trough."

❖ ❖ ❖

Now I took out the ivory comb, delicately carved from a rhino horn. It was my father's present for my eighth birthday.

My father had the soul of an artist. He was never able to resign himself to become a peasant like the rest of his family. He chose to be a peddler, of fine things, he used to say.

For weeks at a time he would travel all over the area, collecting the treasures that village craftsmen would entrust him with for sale in town. His old panel truck, the only one for miles around, made my sisters and me very proud, especially when he took us for a ride around the salt lake, in the heart of the savanna, among the lions and giraffes.

But none of us knew that our daddy wasn't just a peddler: he was also an activist, proud of his ideas and prepared to defend them come what may. And one day, for publicly opposing Haile Selassie before the emperor was destituted, my dear brave daddy was hacked to death with machetes, with no warning and no chance to defend himself.

That was three years before, just after my birthday, and since then, every time I tease out my hair with this comb, I see him smiling at me, and it's still for him that I make myself beautiful.

When I was little, I believed it was possible to climb to heaven with a ladder. Sometimes, I imagined myself climbing up there to visit him, embrace him and tell him that I loved him

The box of treasures

My last treasures, and to me the most precious, were those you left me, Mamina. I know my mother must have had to force herself to include them in my bundle, but she deserves all the more credit for it. You could be proud of your daughter.

There was a red scarf, as red as lobelia flowers, and some ribbons to tie my hair.

A glass pot filled with your all-healing balm, and the medicine bag that your grandmother passed down to you, that you always had with you. It was filled with sachets of wild herbs that we collected together, and whose properties you taught me. There was even some of the soap herb, that would be very useful for me.

But what moved me most was the little school exercise book with your drawings of healing plants. Alongside each one, as you didn't know how to write, you drew the part of the body and the hurts that they could heal.

The following day I would find a stream to see your dear face again, Mamina, and seek the wind to hear your voice. I needed to speak to you, because you alone could give me the strength to survive in that hostile world.

But the sheep were calling for me, and I could not let them wait any longer.

Only the eye of the master can see

Jean de La Fontaine

4

THE MASTER OF THE HORSES

I was exhausted by those first days at Siwa.
Even though I rose at daybreak I didn't manage to complete all my tasks by nightfall.

To gain time, I even missed breakfast, and the midday meal. I contented myself with a few pancakes and some fruit that I carried into my lair in the evening, to keep going until dinner the following day.

That was no hardship, because in the eating hall the servants and grooms regarded me as if I were some curious beast. Apart from Chavha, nobody spoke my language. Perhaps it was better that way, because I could see the looks and secret laughter that showed that I could expect no pity from these people. They were wondering how long a kid like me could last out...

But I did last out, even if I had to grit my teeth. The Lady of Light's words helped me to support the ordeal, and I found I had unexpected resources.

The barefoot princess

The worst of all these completely new tasks was working with the fork. The first night I had bleeding hands. I covered them with your balm, Mamina, and the following day I cut strips of cloth from my torn dress to lessen the pressure of the handle on my sores.

I also used your ointment to treat Chavha's back, which healed completely after a few days.

To thank me, the young girl began to come and help me lift the forkfuls of soiled straw into the bin each day before lunch. She often shared my meager meal, and added a few tidbits filched from the kitchens.

"Here, I've brought you some dates and a few honey cakes that will give you strength ..."

I had already been a week there, and I still hadn't had time to look around the oasis. The next day I promised myself that I would take a little time off from the sheep to go looking for plants and, most important, a river.

I knew that Siwa was full of springs and that the water would be warm at the end of the day. Chavha had promised to take me there that evening, at dinner-time, to be sure that nobody else would be there, so we could bathe in private.

However, though I was tempted by the idea of a swim, my desire to see the horses was even stronger. I felt an increasing passion for these creatures.

But there was no question of asking Chavha to go with me; her terrible warning was still ringing in my ears.

At midday she went to the refectory to bring back some provisions for our nocturnal escapade. I was free.

The master of the horses

I decided to use the opportunity to slip behind the reed fence that hid the horse pen. I was so small I hoped not to be noticed.

The grooms were eating, but the horses were not alone. Dagmar was keeping watch.

Although the master of the horses was dressed in white from head to foot, he was even more terrifying than the man in black. He had the suppleness, the reflexes and the keen eyes of a jaguar. That, at least, was the impression he gave me.

"If you could see him, Mamina, you would certainly say that it's his totemic animal."

I admired the extraordinary beauty of the rider and his mount, a superb black stallion. It was an image of grace and elegance, so perfect, so moving, that seemed to express the essence of harmony.

The two of them seemed to move as one, with the same lightness, in a perfect balance which combined restraint and relaxation, suppleness and firmness, power and delicacy.

It was a dance where both horse and rider were in the same trance. They walked. They trotted. They cantered. It made music to which their hooves, ringing like castanets, gave the rhythm.

Dagmar drew a dozen grays into his dance. The pure bloods slowed or speeded up, executing little side steps, walking, trotting or cantering, their manes flowing in the wind. It was magical!

The barefoot princess

Dagmar had no need to speak: the horses obeyed his directions at a simple click of his fingers, and followed the arabesques of his stallion.

Hidden behind the bamboo, I didn't miss a thing, but nor did I see how late it was. The grooms had already returned to the stables, and then, suddenly.... the accident happened.

A stallion escaped from the paddock and attempted to jump the barbed wire that separated the pen from the mares.

Impaled on the wire, badly hurt, he reared up, whinnying in pain. The groom tried to catch the horse by his bridle, but received a terrible kick in the face and dropped, unconscious, to the ground.

The pure blood was uncontrollable - he was certainly going to kill the groom.

It was more than I could bear. I forgot Dagmar and Chavha's advice. In a moment, I covered the short distance between my hiding place and the horse, and put my hand on his side, glistening with sweat and blood.

He became calm in an instant. But I could sense how much he was suffering: certainly more than the groom, who got up, unhurt except for the imprint of the hoof on his forehead.

I was relieved for the groom, but I knew, alas, the fate reserved for the horse. He had a deep wound in his leg, and this was no place for sentimentality with inured animals.

Preoccupied with calming him, I didn't see Dagmar, who suddenly appeared behind me, like a jack-in-the-box.

The master of the horses

I turned round, to find him standing there with a saber in his hand. I could see in his eyes that he was determined to finish off the animal immediately.

At that moment, I threw myself at his feet, in a mute entreaty, to stop the barbarous gesture.

I expected to be whipped, or even decapitated! But strangely, Dagmar let out a huge laugh. Even more surprisingly, he spoke to me in my dialect. I suddenly felt less afraid.

"I should punish you, finding you here where you have no right to be, but you are courageous, child, and more effective than that idiot," pointing to the groom, who was shaking like a leaf, terrified at the idea of a brutal punishment.

"You want me to spare this horse? Very well, I will give him a respite, but for tonight only.

Tomorrow I shall call in the veterinarian, and if his wound is disabling or leaves ugly scars, he will be shot, because he could never race, nor be sold.

Now... run, cheeky girl, and don't let me see you wandering near my horses again."

I shall never know how Dagmar had guessed that I was Ethiopian, or why he spoke my dialect, but that didn't matter: I had saved the horse, and thanked him by kissing his hand with respect and gratitude.

Then I ran away, but not fast enough to avoid hearing the whimpering of the guilty groom under the lash of the whip.

The barefoot princess

That very evening, after my swim with Chavha and our meal under the stars, I went back alone to the stables. I was sure there must be a way of getting inside without being seen.

I was thin enough to slip in through a skylight, and found myself in a stall, face to face with a chestnut mare, which didn't seem in the least bit bothered by my arrival.

Fortunately, the moon was full and provided enough light for me to find my way in the stables. I finally found the stall with the wounded horse. He was lying on his side, which was not a good sign. Horses only lie down when they are seriously ill.

I had brought Mamina's medicine bag with me, together with her balm, some cloth strips, a handful of green clay that I had collected from the riverbank when Chavha wasn't looking, and some spines from the acacia that grew near the stud farm.

I cleaned the wound gently with water, taken from the drinking trough. The stallion was calm, and accepted my help calmly. Now I had to move on to the most delicate part, bringing the lips of the wound together and closing it with the acacia spines, as my grandmother had taught me when we came across a wounded animal on the savanna.

When the wound was properly sutured, I spread some of Mamina's ointment on it, mixed the clay with some water, dipped my strips in it and rolled them around the torn limb.

The master of the horses

I hoped it would dry and form a plaster to allow the wound to heal without infection. The stallion's head and sides were wet with sweat. He obviously had a fever. So before leaving him, I dipped a piece of cloth in water and rubbed him down with it, asking the healing spirits to relieve his suffering.

His wet, rough tongue lingered on the small of my neck, as if to thank me. It was the first time I had encountered any affection since I had arrived.

❖ ❖ ❖

What happened next was told me by Dagmar himself several weeks later.

The two men were astonished when they discovered my plaster.

"Who did that?!" said the veterinarian.

"I don't know", replied Dagmar

"A groom didn't do that: it's the work of a healer, "said the expert, removing the bandages. "In any event, you can thank the person who did it. The wound is clean and in a few days this horse will be as good as new, with no trace of his injury."

When the veterinarian left, Dagmar noticed, between the horse's hooves, a forgotten pink ribbon...

"That kid is not only gutsy", he said, "She's got more than an ounce of shaman in her. And she's one of my people. I must find a way to help her, or the owners will break her - and she deserves so much better!"

59

Only think that this humble plant that you trample underfoot
is perhaps the bearer of a divine message!

André Gide

5

THE MIRACULOUS BALM

I was so exhausted by the day's emotions, the accident, the strange attitude of the Master of the Horses, my swim in the river with Chavha, and treating the wounded horse, that I collapsed on my bed and fell asleep, without undressing.

I slept, and I dreamt.....

I dreamt that the fine stallion had forgotten his wounds and was carrying me on a wild race through the oasis with his mane flowing and tail rippling.

Shivers ran under his silky coat. His mane, streaming in the wind like a banner, awoke old memories, and I heard again the voice I loved so dearly:

"Do you hear that pace in three-four times, like a waltz? Do you feel it trembling and resounding under your feet? On the fourth beat, your horse almost flies: it's the silence of the canter. Suspended in the air, he comes back to earth on the following step.

The barefoot princess

"Listen ..... now he laughs, lifts up his head and opens his mouth, showing his teeth. That joyful whinny tells you that he is cured. You can be easy in your mind, child, you did what you should."

The joy of hearing Mamina's voice, and the exhilarating feeling of freedom from that mad ride woke me. I was happy. Confident. Reassured. I knew it was not an ordinary dream, but one of those messenger dreams that open the door to other worlds. The spirits, guided by my grandmother, had granted my prayer and the stallion, healed, would escape from his fatal destiny.

As for riding with him, that could only be a figment of my imagination. I wasn't a rider, and even if I were, it was unthinkable that Dagmar, who watched over his stallions with jealous care, would ever allow me to mount one of those superb creatures.

Here, women wore the veil and kept silent: they did not ride horses...

But.... no time to dream, there wasn't a minute to lose, the day was going to be a hard one. The day before, I had overlooked some of my tasks and now I had to catch up on lost time.

I nibbled one of the delicious honey cakes that Chavha had brought for our escapade by the river, then I ran to feed the sheep and the ponies.

I also had to polish the boots and saddles, because the owner's children wouldn't fail to report my negligence if they noticed it. I didn't want to be caught out and punished.

The miraculous balm

While I prepared to strap my hands and feet, bruised by rubbing of the straw and the rocky soil of Siwa, I noticed that Mamina's pot was empty. Treating Chavha and the injured pure blood had used up all my precious ointment.

I would have to go and collect some healing herbs. I had often watched Mamina prepare the balm, and I hoped I had remembered what she had taught me. These memory-gestures, coming from a long line of healing shamans, were my inheritance. The only honor that I had left to me.

I had just fed the animals and polished the saddlery when Chavha came to see me, as she did every day before breakfast.

She was going to grab the fork to help me to change the animals' litter, but I stopped her. I had other things to think about, and all the afternoon to finish my work.

I took out Mamina's exercise book to show her. I pointed to the empty pot and drawings of the plants which made up the ointment: comfrey, lady's mantle and aloe vera, but also rosemary and sage that I had to burn to attract the spirits.

"Comfrey is a herb for treating wounds, child. It heals, prevents wounds from becoming infected, and heals broken limbs.

It also calms the pains of old people like me. When my rusty joints hurt me, I leave the flowers of this excellent herb to macerate in the sun for two days in spring water.

The barefoot princess

Then I soak a square of cotton wool with it, to make compresses which relieve me.

You will recognize comfrey easily, child, its flowers look like little purple or ivory-colored bells. They curl up in spirals and have five little curved teeth that eat pain.

Look closely, Zahia, the leaves of comfrey look like little hairy hearts. Can you feel their stiff hairs rough against your hand? And this stalk, so proud and slender, that has wings like the angels of heaven?"

"Where can I find that plant, Mamina, I haven't seen any around here?"

"Near the salt lake, my sweet, I know it's a long way, but you have strong legs. And you won't have to search for long, comfrey never grows on its own, it lives in groups and forms a carpet with a mauve and pale yellow pattern."

"But Mamina, if I don't have your mule to carry me, my legs will never take me so far!"

"Nothing is for free, Zahia, and your legs will grow. Listen, I will tell you a little story my grandmother told me.

There was a little ant, and its mother said, "Do you see the bush over there? That's where we will find something to eat."

"But the bush is so far! I will never be able to reach it!"

The miraculous balm

"Don't ask questions, just put one foot in front of the other," said the mother ant.

And the little ant obeyed, and reached the bush, without even realizing it.

Do you think you are weaker and less brave than a little ant, Zahia?"

"No Mamina, you are right. And I will not forget your story."

"What you must know, child, for I am not immortal, is that everything in comfrey is good, except the stalk whose sap is an irritant.

Remember, when I prepare the injera, I always add a handful of the fresh leaves of this excellent plant to the vegetables. It replaces the meat that we have so little opportunity to eat, and that helps you to grow without having a bloated stomach like some of your friends who suffer from malnutrition."

"And what is this plant for, Mamina?" I said, pointing to a strong-smelling herb whose leaves were divided into fine strips.

"That's yarrow, child, and it goes very well with comfrey. It has similar qualities and that is why they get on so well.

"According to a Greek legend, the hero Achilles was said to be invulnerable because, on the advice of Athena, goddess of wisdom, he covered his body with the juice of this plant.

Alas, he forgot to rub it on his left heel, and an arrow struck him there and took his life.

You must learn to look, Zahia, it isn't necessary to be a herbalist, or even to know the names of the plants, for each one has its own signature. Its shape, its smell, its taste and the color of its sap tell you all you need to know to relieve and heal the ills of both men and animals.

Look at that wild plant, that scientists call chelidonium. When you pick it, a yellow sap flows from its stalk. What is it like?"

"I may be mistaken, Mamina, but it seems to me that the sap has the acrid, bitter taste, and the color, of bile."

"That's quite correct, child, you are right, and if in doubt ... taste. Plants are not poisoners, and all you risk is a little stomach pain. It doesn't matter much!

"Yes, that plant is excellent for relieving the liver. As for yarrow, it is also called the nose-bleed herb.

It is very useful for me when I visit the spirits because I often have nose-bleeds when I return from the other world. Yarrow stops the bleeding instantly, as water puts out fire.

"Where can I find that plant, Mamina?"

The miraculous balm

"Yarrow always grows close by, on stony wasteland, on the edge of the savanna.

Its heart is a yellow-white tube, from which white or pink flowers grow, and its straight stalk has no branches. You will recognize it by its smell of crushed ants: there is nothing that smells like it.

The third plant that makes my ointment so effective is the aloe vera. It grows in clumps, wherever there is sand, which is why it is called, "the lily of the desert".

The flowers hang in clusters and look like trumpets. Its short stalk carries a bundle of smooth, fleshy green leaves.

It's the leaves that contain the red sap which is so good for treating stomach disorders, tiredness or loss of memory. But it has to be made into decoctions, as I taught you.

The taste is very bitter, and if you don't want your patients to full faces, I advise you to add some honey.

In fact aloes are used to coat the nails of children who bite their nails or suck their thumb - they soon stop because it is so bitter.

However, it is not the sap of the aloe vera that goes into my balm, but its thick red pulp that I obtain by slicing the leaves with my knife.

The barefoot princess

It's the blood of the aloes, and no skin ailment can resist it. Sunburn or chaps, blisters, sprains, open wounds.... it's not called the miracle plant for nothing.

Be careful, though, not to be pricked when you pick it - it has spines."

"Tell me, Mamina, what gives your balm its golden color and makes it so smooth and soft, and so sweet-smelling? It's not just the plants?"

"No, child, it's beeswax. I don't collect it myself; I'm scared to death of the creatures!"

"Dearest Mamina, that is certainly the first time I have heard you say you were afraid of something or somebody."

"You know Zahia, when I was your age, I climbed into the hollow of a tree where there was a wild beehive. I wanted to steal a honeycomb, and I had scarcely had the time to stretch out my hand when I was assailed by a wave of worker bees defending their territory. I was covered in them, from head to foot.

I escaped with just a few stings, but I have never forgotten it, and it is a horrid memory. Since then I prefer to ask Ghanim, the village beekeeper. I exchange a pot of my balm for a bar of his wax for, and we are both of us content."

"What is Ghanim's secret to avoid being stung?"

"He always acts when at sunrise, when the workers have gone to gather pollen, and only the queen is

The miraculous balm

left, with the attendants and the warriors, responsible for her defense. In other words, most of the troops have gone!

Then Ghanim smokes the hive, and the bees think there is a fire, and after taking a provision of honey, they flee, taking the queen with them."

"But ... do they come back afterwards?"

"Yes, as soon as Ghanim has taken the honeycombs and the smoke has gone, the warriors return to see that the hive is intact and the danger is past. Then they escort the queen to her cell and the attendants feed her with royal jelly, a rich white substance that will make her the venerated mother at the next swarm."

"Isn't that very unfair, Mamina, to steal the food that the bees have taken so long to gather?"

"As unfair, child, as killing animals to eat them. It's the law of nature. But Ghanim is not ungrateful - he always leaves some cane sugar to compensate them for the honey he takes from them."

Chavha, who had learnt to respect my heartfelt silences, looked at Mamina's drawings and said to me, pointing at the comfrey:

"I've seen that plant on the banks of the salt lake. This one too," she said, pointing to the yarrow, "It grows everywhere alongside the trails. As for the bushy plant, it can only be found in the desert, and we would have to leave the path ...

It's a long way, Zahia, and we would have to walk for several hours."

The barefoot princess

So there was salt lake here, a forgotten sea, prisoner of the sands, like back home. I was suddenly overwhelmed.... perhaps I would find cowry shells there too.....

The idea gave me wings, and I felt able to walk as much as I had too, like the little ant in the Mamina's story.

"I'll come with you tomorrow evening Zahia, if you like. We'll do as we did when we went swimming, we'll leave when everybody is sitting down for dinner."

I pointed to the sky, and made a gesture of impatience, placing my finger on the drawings in Mamina's exercise book.

Chavha understood that I was worried. Would we be able to find our way when night had fallen, and above all, find the healing plants?

"Don't worry about anything, Zahia, I'll bring a torch that I saw in the butlery, because even if the moon is high and full, the path is stony and it would be stupid to get a twisted ankle. Especially without any ointment!" she added mischievously.

The following evening we walked through crossed Chali, the main village in Siwa, that I had not had the time to visit previously.

The houses were made from tree-trunks and ocher-colored unbaked bricks. Date palms and grey-green olive trees were connected by flowing streams and gushing springs.

Slightly to one side, on a rocky peak, stood strange ruins....

The miraculous balm

"It's the old village", said Chavha, who took her role as guide very seriously, "It was destroyed by heavy rain in the last century. Since then, nobody dares to go there. They believe it is inhabited by lost souls and djinns, who watch out for foolhardy villagers to eat their flesh. Do you believe it?"

I showed her by signs that I did not. Mamina had taught me to avoid the traps set by evil spirits.

"Evil beings, whatever names they are given, only exist if you believe in them, child. Otherwise, they can have no hold on you. Evil goes to evil like water goes to the river, but pure hearts like yours don't interest them. So you don't need to worry about them, leave these superstitions to ignorant people and those who have done wrong."

We met a few women on the path, veiled in black. I gave them a friendly wave, but they turned away, and passed by furtively, without even looking at us. Chavha noticed my surprise.

"No, she said," Here it's not like back home, where the women work in the fields or dress stones like the men. Siwa is a self-contained world, closed to strangers. The Siwans are Berbers, all practicing Muslims, and the customs are very rigid for women.

They don't have the right to go out, or only at night-fall, to collect water with their gourds.

Look, Zahia, this is a hot-water spring, and that is where they come for water for washing and domestic use."

71

The barefoot princess

As soon as we left the village, I discovered the oasis in all its splendor. A sea of golden dunes, lunar landscapes with strange stony concretions, and miles of stony plain.

"This place is a land of legends," said Chavha, "Look over there to the left, it's Mount Ararat, where Bedouins found Noah's Ark.

Just in front is the peak of Sinai, where God dictated the ten commandments to Moses and wrote them in fire on the Tables of Law. Yet it's in our country, at Axoum, that the Ark of the Covenant, which contains them, is buried."

The track through the sand was forbidding and swept by the desert winds, but feeling great emotion we moved on through the immense labyrinth of the white desert.

After walking for an hour, we finally arrived at the salt lake. Around it were vast stretches of eroded shells, amalgamated here and there in strange shapes.

I knew that if I searched, I would soon find some cowries, but I would return for them another day.

"Do you know, Zahia, that we are more than 60 feet below sea-level here? Impressive, isn't it?"

I imagined immense waves covering the desert, like in the story of Moses that Mamina had told me. But I wasn't sure that this god to whom I did not pray would be obliging enough to open the waves to help my escape from Egypt.

The miraculous balm

"You're dreaming again, kid, wake up, because I'm pretty sure your comfrey is there waiting for you..."

A carpet woven from mauve and ivory tracery was spread out before me. Despite the darkness I could see it clearly by the reflection of the moon in the salt lake.

As Mamina, had taught me, I sat down next to the plants, and took the time to breathe calmly to become impregnated with their spirit.

Then I spoke to them, to explain why I needed them. I knew they understood me, even if the words did not leave my lips.

Chavha was intrigued by my ritual, though she remained silent, in order not to disturb my dialogue with the invisible spirits.

After communicating with the plants, I picked them, taking care not to pull up their roots, so as not to kill them.

As a sign of respect and gratitude to their spirit, I left them an offering: one of my ribbons that I buried in the middle of the bed.

That was when I noticed that I only had four of the five ribbons left me by Mamina. I was sure that I hadn't left one in my room. I had mislaid it, there was no doubt about that.

During our swim, perhaps? I dearly hoped so, for otherwise, it must be in the stables...

The barefoot princess

Chavha interrupted my train of thoughts, by pointing to a desert fox who was watching us with his dark eyes.

We tried not to move, and slowly the russet-coated fox became bolder. I could feel he was hungry, and clearly attracted by our food.

I threw a pancake to him, that he ate greedily. Then I tried to communicate with him in thought, as I did with the plants.

To Chavha's immense surprise, he came towards me and accepted a piece of candy, even allowing me to stroke him before running away. But I knew that on my next visit he would be there.

"Well, Zahia, you really have a gift", was all Chavha said.

After this episode, which delighted us, we returned to hunt for yarrow. We had seen some along the stony path, and it would be easy to collect some.

When I had filled Mamina's medicine bag a third full, we accorded ourselves a short pause for dinner on the bank of the salt lake, with only the moon and the stars for company.

"What are the stars, Mamina?"

"They are lights in the sky, child; Each one is an island in the midst of space: it's the backbone of the night. look, some of them always shine with the same light, while others blink or speed off without further ado. Some of them play at spinning tops and try to be cute, while others become frightened and make themselves small: they are shy and are afraid to be seen."

"Why are they not all the same color?"

The miraculous balm

"Because they aren't all the same age. The blue stars are hot and young. The yellow ones are middle-aged and are calmer, and the red ones are approaching their end. As for the little white stars, they are dead, and have been for a long time.

Like the sun and the moon, stars always rise in the east and set in the west. The place where they appear or disappear marks the progress of the seasons.

You should learn their language, because if you can read the movements of the sun, moon and stars, you can tell exactly when it is time to hunt, sow, harvest and collect herbs."

"Don't leave so soon, Mamina, please, there are still so many things you can teach me. I should so much like to become a shaman, worthy of you and the Ancients!"

Now we set off again, to look for the aloe vera. In passing I picked a few branches of spiny rosemary, but the sage seemed to be unknown in the desert. Never mind, my friends the spirits would understand.

The most difficult part was finding the spiny bushes with our torch. The night became darker and denser. The moon now hid discretely behind a veil.

"When the moon wears a halo of mist, it means that it is gibbous, it always happens three days before and three days after full moon. It's the best time to pick herbs, because the moonbeams revitalize them and they fill with sap, which makes them perfect for healing".

75

The barefoot princess

I didn't choose that day to go and collect the herbs for your balm, Mamina, unless.... you guided me from up there, because as you often used to say, *things don't happen by chance...*

We had now left the track and our feet sank into the sand, slowing us. Finally, we found the bushes of aloe vera and despite my precautions and Mamina's warnings, I scratched my hands with the spines.

The way back was difficult. We dragged our feet a little, and as soon as we arrived at my room, I let Chavha go, for she was falling asleep on her feet.

Then I took my plants out of the medicine bag, and spread some of them, those I would use for the balm, on a bed of fresh straw so they would not spoil.

I made little packets with the others, tied with a length of straw and hung head down on the belts which carried the gourds.

I also discovered a little cauldron at the back of the room, which would be very useful, and a box of matches left by Akar. All I now needed was the beeswax, but I would see to that the next day, because I was really too tired.

To recover my strength, I remembered what Mamina had told me, and chewed a few leaves of comfrey. It wasn't very tasty, but getting one's health back had its price!

The following day I tried to explain to Chavha what I needed, and she said:

"I can't get you any beeswax but I know where there are some wild beehives. We could always try ..."

The miraculous balm

I made her understand that we needed to leave at dawn, while the bees are out collecting pollen.

"OK", she said, "I'll be there at 7 o' clock tomorrow morning."

Before going to bed, I prepared a stick around which I wrapped a piece of cloth, the box of matches, a knife and some sachets of cane sugar.

The next morning, when we arrived at the tree where the bees lived, Chavha handed me her flask of olive oil, which I poured on the cloth, and lit the torch, hoping that a servant or groom wouldn't see me.

I waited a few minutes before extinguishing the flame, so as to produce as much smoke as possible. I introduced my torch into the tree and signed to Chavha to follow me. We hid behind the tree.

The bees had understood the danger, and fled, taking the queen with them, easily recognizable because she was ten times bigger than the workers.

Before removing a piece of wax with its honey-filled cells, I addressed a silent prayer to the group-spirit of the bees, to explain the reasons for my gesture.

Was it the smoke or my prayer? I don't know, but no sting interrupted my movements, although a few warriors remained in the hive, ready to make the ultimate sacrifice...

To thank the bees and so that they would forgive my theft, I left the contents of the sugar sachets, which I hoped would be appreciated, at the entrance to the hive.

The barefoot princess

We returned to my room to prepare everything. I stuck the rosemary branches in the cracks in the wal and lit them, to call the spirits so they would be favorable to us.

Then we made a hearth, surrounded by a few big stones to prevent the fire from spreading, tied two sticks together and hung Akar's cauldron from it.

Chavha went to fetch water from the sheep's trough, and I prepared the fire.

Fed with straw, it caught quickly. Chavha poured in the water, and when it began to sing I threw in the comfrey and yarrow flowers.

While they were simmering, I slit the aloe vera leaves with my knife to remove the pulp.

When all the pulp had been poured into the boiling cauldron, we took it off the fire, and I dropped the wax, wrapped in a piece of cloth, into the boiling water to soften it.

We waited until the water had cooled a little to avoid scalding our hands, then removed the bag and squeezed the remaining juice from the plants.

I took some of this brew to mix it with the wax, and stirred it with a stick so that it was well mixed.

To finish, I poured the mixture carefully into Mamina's pot and closed it, hoping that by morning, when it would be cold and thickened, it would have the same smoothness and the same scent as that prepared by my grandmother, and above all, would be as effective.

The miraculous balm

As Chavha left me she said:

"Zahia, I will never forget what I experienced tonight. Now I'm sure that you are a shaman, and I know that she who taught you these marvelous secrets is watching you from above and is proud of you."

It was the first time that I had felt a presence, that of Mamina, so strongly. Perhaps she came to pass me the torch!

The truth of a being is first of all what he hides

André Malraux

6

I BECOME "ANOTHER"

When I put my foot on the ground, I was unable to keep from calling out, the pain was so intense.

I hadn't realized, the previous evening when we left the track, that the desert sand never loses its fire, even at night, and the soles of my feet were covered in blisters.

"Take care where you walk, Zahia, the soles of my feet are protected by hard skin, as thick and tough as the feet of the animals of the savanna, but yours are still tender, and when you run or climb trees like a little monkey, you might well hurt yourself!"

You were quite right, Mamina, and now I couldn't even manage to stand upright.

This was an opportunity to see whether the balm I had prepared the previous night would be effective enough to relieve my pain. But, before testing it, I needed an acacia spine to pierce the swollen blisters.

The barefoot princess

It was a real exploit to reach the hook where I had hung the acacia branch. I hopped from one foot to the other so that it would hurt less, then sat on the edge of my bed and let out a deep breath. It hurt, but I felt some relief as soon as the blisters emptied.

I opened the jar impatiently, and I was pleased to see that its color, smoothness and scent were very similar to that of Mamina's balm. It only remained to see if it was as miraculous.

I spread it thickly over my feet and wrapped them with the last strip of the torn dress that I was wearing when I arrived. I would have to ask Chavha if she could find me an old sheet to use for lint.

When my feet looked like those of an Egyptian mummy, I went to the door to get some fresh air. It was very necessary, because as soon as the sun rose, the cool night air became burning hot.

There was a package on the ground, very visible in front of my door. There was no name written on it: was it for me? Or had somebody made a mistake?

The day before I had told Chavha that the following day was my 12th birthday: had she got up early to give me a surprise? If so, why didn't she knock and give it me herself?

I opened the box and discovered a pair of dancing shoes, exactly like those worn by ballerinas!

I had once seen a picture of a dancer in my school book, and that had made me dream a lot.

I become "another"

These shoes were obviously my size, and though my bandages prevented me from trying them there and then, I knew they would fit me perfectly.

For now, I contented myself with admiring their fineness and especially, their suppleness. I had never worn any, but I had often envied my school friends, from better-off families, like the children of the teachers who came from town, and never went barefoot.

But their shoes were nothing to compare with those I held in my hand. Theirs were stiff and hard, and those that Danna, one of my friends, had allowed me to try one day had hurt my feet.

Where had Chavha been able to find such a marvel? Had she stolen them from the daughter of the owner's wife? That seemed unlikely, because I had already waxed her boots in the saddlery, and they were much bigger.

As I turned one of the little shoes in my hand, something fell on the ground: it was one of Mamina's pink ribbons, the one I preferred, and had lost. Had Chavha found it and forgotten to give it back to me? Surely not, because she couldn't have gone to the river after our evening together, it was too far and she was so tired.

There had to be another explanation: the stables! But I didn't even dare think about that possibility, because it would mean I had been found out, and in that case I didn't dare imagine the punishment Dagmar would have in store for me ...

Chavha knocked on my door at that moment ... I would have the answer, and I trembled in anticipation because I had the feeling that she had nothing to do with my present!

The barefoot princess

After kissing my friend, I showed her the pretty shoes, and she immediately replied to my questioning look:

"No Zahia, it's not me. I have never worn such fine shoes, even on Sundays", pointing to her sandals, no more than soles held on by laced ribbons.

I had no time to ask myself any other questions, because somebody else knocked on my door. It was a young Egyptian servant, who told me to follow her at once.

As I didn't go fast enough for her liking, she grabbed my arm roughly and dragged me towards the building which housed the refectory.

Dagmar's house was just next to it, an impressive mansion made of pink bricks, surrounded by palm trees. My intuition was correct. I expected the worst...

What intrigued me the most was the strange reason that had made the master of the horses send me that present, while there was no doubt that he had every intention of punishing me severely.

I remembered how the negligent groom had been treated, and tears came into my eyes, despite myself.

"Human beings are like animals, child. When they sense that you are afraid, it makes them nasty. control your feelings and they will switch on the charm."

Standing before me like a rock, Dagmar was even more impressive than when he was on his horse. I had not really looked at him before, but now he seemed huge and terribly menacing.

84

I become "another"

Nevertheless, in a flash of pride, I dared to look him in the eye. I could see no anger. No malice.

"Good day, Zahia, I see that you haven't put on my shoes" he said, pointing to my bandaged feet. "No doubt you have hurt yourself ? But, if I can go by the condition of Medina, the horse you treated so skillfully, you know what to do and it won't last for very long..."

Yes, child, he is healed, and he is gamboling as before, and the veterinarian has assured me that he will have no aftereffects of the accident. That is why I had you brought to me.

First of all, let me tell you that the fact you are dumb is not a problem for me. I know you are not deaf, and that your condition is caused by a shock, it's not due to your birth. So if you wish to reply to my questions, or simply speak to me, all you have to do is pronounce the words, as before, and I will be able to read your lips.

You know that I speak your language, but you must keep it to yourself, because here, apart from the master who knows all about my past, people think I am an Egyptian born and bred, and that's how it must remain.

I know you have a strong character and you do what you want when you think it is right. You don't care about any punishment you might receive, even though you know I'm not soft-hearted...

Your courage is to your credit, child, but I don't like it. I expect complete obedience from those who serve me, and if not, I know how to crush the spirits of rebels.

The barefoot princess

The reason you are here is this: it's the gift I have detected in you. I asked the owners to let me take you into my service.

I have to tell you that they burst out laughing. They even thought that I have a taste for little girls. Don't worry - I assure you that is not so!

'This Zahia' they said, 'Is only good for menial tasks, and our horses are the most precious things we have. There is no question of letting her come into contact with them, especially as she is dumb, Ethiopian and a girl, as well.'

To defend your cause I had to explain how you had saved Medina, and assure them that I didn't want to make a groom of you, but a servant.

Nevertheless, I added that there is no doubt at all that you have the gifts of a healer, and will be able to help me with the foaling of the four mares who are near their term. The veterinarian doesn't live in the oasis and the grooms have no nursing ... it is a risk.

The owner thought about it. The idea of losing a mare or a foal was a weighty argument for him. 'I have total confidence in you, Dagmar', he said, 'And I give you carte blanche, even if what you ask seems very strange to me.

It won't be difficult to replace that girl. She can take on her new functions today. I have a boy who can take over from her at once.'

I become "another"

Then he changed his mind, and to convince him to let you come into contact with the horses I had to promise that you would never reveal your identity and your beliefs, and that you would dress like a young boy so avoid attracting attention.

He finally accepted, saying:

'I married an Englishwoman myself, that proved I am not prejudiced. But I don't want to create problems in the stables by introducing a child who is not of our world. Do as you think fit, Dagmar, but understand that at the least problem with this girl, you risk your own position'.

So what do you think, child, are you ready to play the game and respect all my demands, or do you prefer to go back to your sheep?"

I replied, trying to speak clearly so that Dagmar could read my lips:

"That suits me perfectly, Master. I will try to be docile and please you. I'm happy and proud to work for you, even if to do so I have to disguise myself as a boy."

"I must warn you", replied Dagmar, "That I will not tolerate any rebellion from you. You must follow my orders to the letter and carry out all the tasks I will require of you. Some of them may seem strange but I expect complete submission from you: will you be able to do so?"

I nodded to show that I agreed. I knew that it would not always be easy to work for Dagmar, but the idea of being able to be close to the pure bloods every day filled me with joy.

The barefoot princess

The only problem was Chavha. Would I be able to see my friend again? I doubted it, because I had understood that I would have to leave my little room and live in one of the outbuildings of Dagmar's house. I would have to be available at any moment.

As if he could read my thoughts, the horse master added:

"I have also asked the owner to take Chavha into my personal service. He has granted me that favor but before employing your friend I must speak to her because I must be sure that she will be as silent as you, and won't reveal your identity or your functions.

Now, child, I am going to tell you something that will certainly hurt your pride. I spoke to the owner about your wages, and replied:

'We bought this girl on the recommendation of Father Gilles and we paid a high price. So there is no question of wages: it is she who is indebted to us.'

What you must understand, Zahia, is that you are not a servant here like Chavha: you are a slave.

I know, it's cruel. I don't like what happened. That priest, man of god though he may be, is just a human flesh merchant. He doesn't choose poor little girls by charity, but purely by greed.

Your mother only received a handful of *birrs*, but he pocketed more than twice as much.

Unfortunately, I can do nothing about it. At least, for the present. If I had insisted, the owner would have refused to let me take you into my service. I'm not rich, I won't be able to pay you personally, but I will ensure that you never lack anything.

I become "another"

On the other hand, Zahia, rest assured that at the least error I will show you no favors: you will feel my whip just like the others, and if it should happen, never think it is because you are a slave, but simply because I demand absolute obedience and faithfulness.

So, if you agree to conclude our pact and obey my orders, stay there and take one pace forward. Otherwise, take a step back and return to your tasks."

I didn't need to reply. The stars shining in my eyes spoke for me. I took a step forward.

"That's perfect, child, and from now on your name will be Zahiel... when I have seen Chavha and I am assured of her silence, you will both be able to bring your things. Meanwhile, I will show you the room that you and your friend will share."

When I saw the place that Dagmar had reserved for us, I was filled with wonder. The immaculately white walls were decorated with little frames holding drawings of flowers. There were two real beds, covered in colored sheets, a big cupboard for our clothes, and even pink curtains at the windows.

"The shower and rest-rooms are just next door," said Dagmar, "There is hot water and you'll find towels in this cupboard.

Chavha will prepare the meals for you both and for me, and you will eat in this kitchen. It's not very big, but it has modern equipment and even a fridge.

Now I'm going to leave you alone, while I talk to

Chavha. That will give you time to get to know your new environment."

When Dagmar had gone, I found that the cupboards in the kitchen, and the fridge, were brimful with provisions. I even offered myself the luxury of serving a glass of fresh guava juice.

The interview with Dagmar went very well for Chavha. When she appeared, alone, at the door of our bedroom, I could see that she was as surprised and happy as I was. That really pleased me, because I had been afraid that she would miss her work in the kitchens or that she would be afraid of serving the master whom she so dreaded.

"You know, we are alone here", she said, "It's amazing, but to keep your secret, the master has dismissed the usual servants, and he threatened to cut out my tongue at the least indiscretion. It makes me shudder to think about it!"

Chavha looked so terrified as she said this that I burst out laughing. I couldn't really imagine Dagmar cutting out my friend's tongue with his saber.

My laughter was contagious and we were soon both doubled up, hilarious, on our beds, which were so comfortable that we nearly fell asleep.

"By the way, Zahia, doesn't it bother you, dressing as a boy?"

I shook my head, and that somewhat surprised her. But of course she was almost sixteen, and she was beginning to get interested in men. Where I came from she would probably have been married before that age, and perhaps even a mother already.

I become "another"

"I'm so happy to be able to share this lovely bedroom with you, Zahia", she said, "In the owners' house I slept on a straw mattress in the same room as the four servants, who treated me as their whipping girl. Imagine how different it's going to be for me!

For me you are much more than a healer: you're a magician!

Dagmar told me the story of the wounded horse, and even if I hold it against you, just a little, for taking so many risks despite my warnings, I understand the master's leniency now.

I think he has discovered your powers and he knows how useful you will be for his horses. It's his whole life, do you see, and though he has the reputation of being violent and cruel sometimes, they also say he is a just man.

Anyway, we'll see ... meanwhile we would do well not to upset him."

We decided to move our things that afternoon. When I was packing my bundle, I had a thought for Akar, and to avoid them falling into impious hands, I took down the image of his Christ and my mother's cross, and slipped them into my box of treasures.

I also went to feed the sheep, because I wasn't sure that my replacement would be there immediately, and I didn't want them to suffer as they did when I arrived.

As soon as we had put away our things, Chavha went to look at the provisions, to prepare our dinner and that of Dagmar. as I had nothing to do, I gave her a hand. My friend was in ecstasy. She had never seen so much food.

The barefoot princess

"There's enough here to feed a whole village" she cried.

Neatly stored in the cupboard, all sorts of spices and cereals presented themselves to our greedy eyes: barley, brown rice, pilpil, beans, chick peas, olive oil, flour and even dry biscuits.

The contents of the fridge were even more impressive: meat balls and kebabs, stuffed vine leaves, young pigeons ready for roasting and vegetables and fruit a-plenty.

We prepared a starter with cucumber and fresh mint, laced with yoghurt and lime, a few lamb kebabs, accompanied with crusty rice and a choice of fresh fruit: mangos, papaya, guavas and pineapples, which Chavha peeled and cut into little cubes while I arranged them prettily in a dish.

Dagmar seemed satisfied with his meal, even if he didn't utter a word. I was prepared to bet that to obtain a compliment from him would be infinitely more difficult than to tame a desert fox...

"You must present yourselves at 7am tomorrow morning", he told us, "and I will give you your tasks for the day.

I'm counting on you, Zahia. Be on time, and properly dressed. But now I think of it, do you have an alarm clock?" and he added, glaring at us:

"I will not tolerate a single minute's lateness".

I become "another"

Chavha told him that we didn't have one but we were used to rising with the sun.

Dagmar left for a few minutes and came back with a device neither of us had seen before.

"It's a radio alarm", he said," I will program it for you for 6:30 and it will wake you with music. As long as you don't touch the button that I have just set, you can even listen to music in your room in the evenings. Your room is isolated and you won't disturb anyone."

I was walking on air. I missed music so much since Mamina had left me.

"Look, this is a krar, it was left to me by my grandmother. Its double handle, carved out of a branch, allows me to hold it correctly, even if my old hands are as knotted as the roots of the master- tree. Its body is made from a tortoise-shell, on which a goatskin has been stretched. When its five strings are plucked, they produce music that enchants the spirits. Listen...."

And my grandmother drew from her instrument sounds so melodious that they awoke dreams and opened doors to other worlds....

I would so like to have kept your lyre for myself, Mamina, but the day after you left us, mother threw it on the fire, saying:

"That will make a nice blaze and chase away the spirits of evil !"

That day I wept a lot, and until this evening I had thought that the magic world of sounds was closed to me for ever.

The barefoot princess

Certainly, the music that flowed from Dagmar's radio did not have the same purity or the same flight but it made me happy, for in each note, it was a little of my Mamina who lived again.

❖ ❖ ❖

I didn't wait for the alarm to ring: I was so excited by my new life that I went to bed before we had prepared breakfast.

I had never had a hot shower, and it was a real delight. The soap smelt beautifully of olive oil, while the towels were as soft as lamb's wool and their caress on my skin felt wonderful.

I spread my balm on the soles of my feet, which were already almost healed. I found some gauze and some adhesive cloth tape to maintain the dressing in place. It was light enough to wear Dagmar's pretty shoes for the first time.

I put on my gandura, which was as white as the master's, and carefully hid my hair under the traditional turban.

I looked in the mirror, and found that I really looked like a little boy, which didn't displease me.

Finally, I took a tray and placed on it a glass of guava juice, a teapot, a jug for hot water, a smaller one for the milk, a few pieces of sugar and some donuts that I had found in the fridge. I couldn't resist the temptation to eat one - it was delicious!

I become "another"

When Chavha had finished her shower, all she had to do was to heat the liquids, because I didn't know how to work the oven.

When the alarm sang out, Chavha had breakfast, got ready and took Dagmar his tray. The master told her what tasks she had for the day, and she withdrew so as not to disturb our tête-à-tête.

"Here's what you are going to do this morning, Zahia", he said, giving me an exercise book, a pen and a book in Arabic.

I didn't understand a thing, of course, but there were drawings opposite each word, like Mamina's book. It was a book for little Egyptian children to learn to read.

"I want you to learn this language, Zahia. You have one month to learn the 300 essential words that will allow you to understand what is being said around you.

Every morning, you will learn 10 new words. And don't think of taking it easy, child, because I will test your progress every week.

You must not only memorize them perfectly, but also know how to write them. For the pronunciation, ask Chavha, she has a rudimentary knowledge of Arabic."

"Why, master? I'm dumb. You are the only one who can read my lips."

"Do as I say, Zahia, I know you will soon get your voice back, and when it happens you must be ready.

Now I'm going to talk about something which may displease you.

The barefoot princess

However, you must obey me: you promised me.

I want you to understand the basics of Islam. It doesn't matter whether you believe it or not. You must be able to respect the customs here.

Of course, I'm going to arrange things so you will be in contact with the others as little as possible, but you won't always be able to avoid it. You must prostrate yourself like them, facing the earth, when the muezzin calls to prayer. That will avoid you being found out."

Dagmar could see that this didn't please me at all.

"That's not the attitude of a true shaman, Zahia; gestures have little importance, because in the secret of your soul, you pray to whom you wish: the spirits, or ... your grandmother's manna, for example! They must never suspect that you are Christian, and even less that you are animist.

Here, Muslim law requires that horses are only in contact with those who venerate the Prophet. I had to comply with these rites myself. If you don't do so, you will be accused of witchcraft and I will be obliged to dismiss you, if you don't want to be lapidated!"

The horse twitched its nostrils
Then whinnied as if to the firmament
And surrounding itself with illusion
Gave itself up to its gallop.

Jules Supervielle

7

DAGMAR'S INITIATION

"This afternoon", Dagmar said to me, "I will begin to teach you about pure bloods, because even if you have a gift, there are a lot of things you don't know."

"When will I be allowed to see them, master?"

"In a few days, when the employees are asleep, I'll take you to see the mares that are in foal. They are going to foal soon and I want to teach you how you can help me when the time comes.

You may not have noticed, but there is a bell in your room, which is connected directly to my house. You must practice getting dressed very quickly, even at night, because the mares are in the habit of foaling between midnight and four in the morning. I'll warn you as soon as the warning signs begin to appear.

Don't lose any time. You can go and have breakfast, and ask Chavha to serve me."

The barefoot princess

Lunch, with a main course of young pigeons that Chavha had simmered in a casserole with barley, was a real feast. My friend managed very well alone in the kitchen and the master seemed to appreciate it.

After the traditional tea, Dagmar sat at his desk with me in front of him and spread out some superb books, filled with photos of Egyptian pure bloods.

❖ ❖ ❖

"Let's start with the legend, Zahia, because it can often teach us more than history can.

When Allah decided to create the horse, he said to the south wind,

'Condense, so that out of you I will create a new being to glorify those who serve me and to humiliate my enemies'...

and the south wind replied,

'Lord, be its creator'.

Allah took a handful of the south wind, blew upon it and said,

"I name you Horse; you will be called Arab,
and I give you the brown color of the ant.
You will be the lord of the other animals,
and men will follow you wherever you go.
You will be as brave in attack as in retreat.
You will fly without possessing wings.
The rich will mount you
and fortune will smile on them thanks to you."

Dagmar's initiation

Then he gave the horse the mark of glory and happiness: a white star in the midst of its forehead.

Medina, the horse you saved, has that white star. That is why he is worth so much. There are only three of them marked with the seal of Allah in this stud farm, and the desert emirs and princes, when they come to Siwa, are ready to spend a fortune to own them.

Other pure bloods that you can see in this book, which was produced here in this very stud farm, have a white patch on the neck, and are also very much sought after, because it is said that they bear the mark of the Prophet.

The Koran tells us that Mohammed possessed a troop of mares that he loved greatly, and one day he decided to put them to the test, to evaluate their submission and their courage. He left them several days without drinking. When he freed them, they galloped to the river to quench their thirst, but just before they got there, he called them back. Only five mares returned immediately, and those five are said to be the ancestors of the entire race.

To recognize these five exceptional horses, and their descendants, the Prophet marked their necks with his thumb. A dimple called the Thumb of the Prophet.

The Prophet thought that the pure-bred Arab was unquestionably superior to the other horse breeds. He understood that the mission of conquest he had bequeathed to his people could only be accomplished by bold horsemen and it was necessary to develop a love of horses at the same time as faith in Islam.

The barefoot princess

So that the Bedouin would keep the race pure, all the religious passages concerning the Arab horse were written in a colorful, poetic style in order to convince Muslims that they are God's elected and the horse was created only for them.

The Koran uses poetry to place the horse on a pedestal. It promises the horse owner the "goods of this world" and clearly expresses the wish that only a Muslim may mount an Arab horse.

It makes it clear that for a pure-bred Arab to sacrifice himself for its master in war or work, it is necessary to make it happy and treat it with tenderness.

The Prophet also promised rewards to the owners of pure-bred Arabs to encourage them to respect the purity of their horses.

So it is difficult to separate the Arab horse from the Muslim religion, as its breeding is considered to be a religious duty, even today. It is even forbidden for a Muslim to demand money to cover a mare, to promote breeding and improve the breed. In the same way, it is forbidden to castrate a horse, or even to take its mane or its tail, which enable him to protect himself from flies.

Do you now understand, Zahia, why you must be so careful? Not only you're not Muslim, but you are also a woman: that makes you doubly impure!

Dagmar's initiation

Now I am going to leave you to take in these pictures. Here is another book, which shows different breeds of horse. I will question you later to see whether you have retained the specificities of the true pure blood Egyptian.

For me it is important that you learn to look, as your grandmother taught you."

How did Dagmar know that? I had never spoken to him about Mamina! Was this man a seer? Could he read my thoughts?

"Yes" continued my master, "I don't yet know what I am going to do with you, but you must learn to recognize instantly a true Egyptian pure blood from an imitation."

Alone again, I looked closely at the books and applied myself to noting everything I could in my exercise book.

For instance, I wrote that the Arab horse has 17 thoracic vertebrae instead of 18 and 6 for other breeds.

His coat is usually grey, but some are bay, chestnut like Medina, or black, like Dagmar's horse.

The head of the Egyptian Arab is small and expressive. His forehead is wide and his small, mobile ears are attentive to the least noise or breath of wind. His dark brown eyes are large and prominent. He has large nostrils and slim lips.

Then I looked at his body: it was like a jigsaw puzzle of which I was putting the pieces together. The neck is long, wide and arched. The withers are prominent, the chest well-muscled and the shoulder is sloping. The croup is ample and horizontal.

The barefoot princess

The limbs are loose and slim and his hooves are small and hard. The Arab's tail is held high and its hairs are long and abundant. His veins show through his fine skin, as I had already noticed when treating Medina.

When Dagmar returned I told him what I had learnt, and he seemed impressed.

"You have a keen eye. We're going to work well together". Then he added, half to himself:

"You see, it wasn't the legend that first impressed me when I saw a pure blood Arab for the first time. That is only true for Muslims. No, it was the aura he had, that shows so clearly the source of the blood that flows in his veins. I had the feeling that I was close to that original source.

When I looked into his eyes, saw the brilliance of his coat, felt the fine delicacy of his skin, and saw the immense strength that his blood-line gave to every part of his body, I was transported to a far universe, by an oasis fed by clear water. I didn't know then that it would be Siwa....The whole body of the pure blood shivered as I approached. His brilliant eye fixed on the horizon, and he seemed to be contemplating infinity. That day, I knew that all my life would be devoted to serving him.

That is what an educated eye sees in the authentic Egyptian Arab horse, Zahia. There is nothing that can compare with that feeling".

Dagmar's initiation

My initiation was beginning, and I, little Zahia - that Dagmar would call Zahiel in public, to avoid any suspicion - I had just found the master I dreamt of. I was sure that my grandmother was not unconnected with this new-found happiness.

After that brief moment of elation to express his passion, Dagmar said to me:

"Zahia, you are free now - I know you want to pick other herbs, so I will show you a place where you can store them. You could even set up a little laboratory to prepare your decoctions and your ointments, with all discretion of course.

Return when you wish to, I know that gathering plants takes a lot of time. You may even take Chavha with you. I won't be here this evening."

"And what about the mares, master?"

"Don't worry; the veterinary has assured me that they won't foal for a day or two yet."

The little room that Dagmar showed me was ideal for drying my herbs, and there were even hooks on the ceiling for me to hang them to dry. But it was covered with spider webs, and cluttered with empty boxes and bottles. I decided to ask Chavha to give me hand to clear everything out and clean the place up.

We got down to work enthusiastically, and the dark little room was soon sparkling clean. However, I had to calm my friend's enthusiasm, who wanted to crush unwelcome inhabitants, who, having lost their webs, were running all over the place.

The barefoot princess

"Don't kill creatures unnecessarily, child, they have a soul as you do, and afterwards you won't be able to speak to their group spirit. Even the smallest has its use in the great chain of life".

So I showed my friend how to collect the spiders on a cloth and free them outside. They would soon find somewhere else to spin their webs.

At the back of the room we discovered a little stove, which would be ideal for my future preparations, and a little shelf where I could store my ointment.

After, we got ready for a long walk that would allow me to fill the medicine bag. Chavha also brought a bigger bag along, hoping that our crop would be fruitful.

I also brought Mamina's precious exercise book. Though I had often accompanied my grandmother to collect herbs, it was more than four years ago, and I was afraid not to be able identify correctly the plants we would find.

The medicine bag and Chavha's bag were soon full to bursting, and we prepared to go back, to unpack our treasures and inaugurate our herb room.

As we walked through Chali, we surprised a group of Siwis standing around a man who had fallen and had dislocated his shoulder. It was very painful but I knew how to deal with it. I went up to the man, and before the astonished villagers, I put his shoulder back in place with one sharp movement. He let out a loud cry but when he realized that he could move his arm normally, he allowed me to rub his shoulder with Mamina's ointment and make a sling for his shoulder with my scarf.

Dagmar's initiation

The villagers encircled me and in their eyes I could see their respect, gratitude and also.... fear.

The man I had treated, who naturally took me for a boy, said a few words to me in Amazigh, the local dialect. Chavha translated:

"This man says that if you wish, you could go with him tonight to a ceremony with the spirits that will be held in the abandoned village. He also says that you must go there alone".

Chavha, somewhat angry, added, "Anyway, Zahia, don't count on me, because that place frightens me, and ... it's full moon!

I nodded to thank the man, who understood. He knew I would go.

Let the Universe perish, as long as I revenge myself!

Cyrano de Bergerac

8

THE EVIL CEREMONY

Hundreds of lanterns little lamps flickered in the windows of the red earth houses, worn by the water. The souls of victims of the flood, waking under the round eye of the moon.

The ancient village of Chali was coming back to life to the dull rhythm of the drums, inhabited by memories and perhaps also by a few djinns who were on the watch for new victims.

Although we had not set a time for our meeting, the villager was waiting for me. I recognized him by his arm in the sling made from my red scarf.

He took my hand in a fatherly gesture, which made me start, not being used to such familiarity, but for him I was a boy, and the gesture seemed natural. .

Before going inside, the man showed me that I should purify myself, in a sort of tub placed there for that purpose.

The barefoot princess

Fortunately it was only a foot bath, or I would have had to reveal my true identity.

After this ritual we went into the place of worship in bare feet, without drying them.

The ceremony took place in a kind of square shed, with a floor of beaten earth. In the centre stood an altar supporting a crude statue with a grimacing expression.

It was daubed with red paint and its sniggering mouth seemed to feed the fire that burnt in the centre of a circle.

"Exu", said my guide. In his look shone the pride of those who had created an idol.

To our right stood drummers and other musicians stood, while in the centre of the circle of flames, surrounded by sea-shells, a man appeared, like an ironmaster. He was impressively built and he drew strange signs on the floor with his sword.

A violet veil hid his face, and his body was covered in a sort of cape, decorated with feathers and amulets, like those worn by the medicine-men in my country.

Was it a birds' cloak to seek souls in suffering in the spirit world? Was this man a shaman?

There was no time to learn more, because the master of ceremony had already disappeared into the wings of his shadow theatre, defined by a black sheet, like the draperies of the mess for the dead.

The evil ceremony

After a long frightening silence, the drums began again, while outside, chanting women approached: a dozen singers, all old women, with their hair hanging freely down their backs, wearing white blouses with broad sleeves, entered the room one after the other.

Each of them held a lighted black candle in her right hand. When they arrived in front of the statue of Exu, they lay the candles at its feet and lit bitter-smelling incense that got to my throat.

I had difficulty in breathing but they continued to sing, apparently unbothered, and without allowing themselves to be distracted by the other people present, who stayed perfectly still in the half-light inhabited by palpable presences.

I realized that the singers were in a trance, when I saw the eyes of one of them, rolled upwards, by the light of the candle she was holding. They were in communication with the spirits and had lost all contact with the living.

I knew that state well, having experienced myself several times, but I had an obscure feeling that these spirits had no relationship with those of Mamina.

As soon as the lament had ceased, the women stood around in a half-circle and held out their arms to the entrance, in a gesture that seemed like an entreaty.

This was when the master of the spirits appeared again. He had removed his bird cloak, and was now bare-chested. His musculature was impressive and his bronze body was covered with signs identical to those he had drawn on the ground.

The barefoot princess

His ritual markings were not white, like those of shamans or warriors, but blood red. His hair was hidden under a black turban and his face was still masked by a violet scarf.

He prostrated himself in front of the altar to Exu, which seemed to be alive in the flickering light of the dark candles.

The master of spirits spoke to the red god. From his lips came a soft, grave invocation, which quickly gave place to guttural, almost inhuman sounds.

Savage onomatopoeia tore the night, punctuated by the staccato beating, ever more rapid, of the drums.

Suddenly the man rose, letting out a great cry, and ran out of the room, followed by the priestesses.

The drums fell silent, and a fearful silence fell upon the petrified audience. Nobody dared move. Then, as if a mysterious fluid had inspired them, the musicians bent once more over their drums, which began to beat frantically again.

The singers returned, and a slow savage rhythm, beaten vigorously on the skin of a large drum, pounded the sky. The moon filtered through the ragged palm fronds of the roof, devoured by the rains.

The evil ceremony

Suddenly, the grave sound of a tuba began to tremble, movingly naive, and moved the bodies to dance. The audience mingled with the possessed, and held their hands, forming a kind of round dance. As the rhythm became livelier, a trumpet called. Their bodies become languid, and become more and more lascivious. This insistent music carried within it centuries of black magic and obscene voluptuousness.

The dancers were in a trance, under the influence of a bewitching spell. My neighbor tried to drag me into that mad dance, but I shook my head, and he did not insist. He thought no doubt that I was too young and impressionable.

In fact, I was very ill at ease. This ritual was nothing like the shamanic sessions that I had attended with Mamina.

Shamanism carries man toward the divine; It is an act of faith and of power that makes the shaman the equal of the gods. Whereas this savage ceremony, an invitation to the imbalance of all the senses, was a consenting abandonment to a power that attempted to become incarnate. The god that was invoked here, for what reason, I still did not know - had certainly no healing vocation. But I was soon to have my answer.

Now the master of spirits held a doll that he covered in ashes, and presented it to Exu. He pronounced a litany like an execration and to my great surpise, I understood what he was saying : he spoke my language and his words made me go cold:

The barefoot princess

"I transfer your essence into the body of this little doll. By the power of similarity you are now one with her. You name is now known to the spirits. I have you in my power for as long as I wish it."

By the light of the flames, I could make out a crudely drawn Coptic cross, like that which my mother had given me.

The sorcerer - what else could I call him! - drove a nail into the heart of the fetish, saying:

"It is now your turn to suffer.
For so I have decided".

And he punctuated this savage gesture with an insane laugh, which resembled the neigh of Medina when he was impaled on the barbed wire.

But the worst was yet to come. Now the man came towards me and dropped the evil statuette at my feet, like an offering.

He made a sign that I should pick it up, and I obeyed, despite myself. When I looked up, I recognized, in the dilated golden pupils, the eyes of Dagmar.

My heart suddenly beat wildly, and I fled in a panic, carrying the doll with me. I had to do something.

❖ ❖ ❖

Back in my room, I looked closely at the cursed doll. Its shoulders were covered by a cloth: a piece of priest's chasuble. A name was written in *Gueze* above the Coptic cross: Father Gilles.

The evil ceremony

There was not a minute to lose. I searched in the kitchen cupboards and found a bottle of white rum, that I poured over the statuette before striking a match and lighting it, to melt the hot wax.

Then I ran to the nearest spring, to entrust the melted wax to it.

The water became cloudy, and before being carried away by the current, the wax drew two yellow eyes in the moonlight, like those of a jaguar.

"You did what you should, my child!"

"No Mamina, there is no reason to be proud of me because my heart is impure. I did not destroy that statuette to save Father Gilles, but only to save Dagmar's lost soul".

9

THE ROOTS OF EVIL

When I returned from my nightly escapade, I did not return to my room immediately. I didn't know if Chavha was asleep, and I didn't want her to sense my terror and my grief. I didn't wish to reveal Dagmar's secret to anybody, not even to my friend.

Only Mamina could hear me and guide me. So I went to take refuge in the shed where the herbs were kept, to invoke my grandmother.

I hoped that she would come, because I had never felt so lost. I had never needed her so much. My heart was full of doubt, questions, sorrow, yes and anger too.

Mamina, I knew that in this place there was neither the murmur of the wind, nor the mirror of still water to reflect your dear presence, but I hoped that my magic cowry and the beating of my heart would be enough to bring you to me.

The barefoot princess

"I'm here my child. Your distress and your grief have called up my soul. I know what you saw, and I know what confuses you so much.

I am going to help you to see beyond appearances. Speak, Zahia, you heart must free itself".

"Mamina, I had complete confidence in Dagmar. I thought he was good and just, despite his impetuous and dominating character.

I saw him as a benefactor, perhaps even the father I no longer have. The initiator sent by you and the spirits to light the way for me.

But I saw him practicing a terrible rite. Black and violent magic. Now, I don't know whether I must love him, fear him or hate him.

Do you see, Mamina, I thought he had chosen me for my gifts. To help him to care for his horses. But now I wonder if it wasn't just to pervert my gift and draw me down a path that is not mine.

Perhaps he is going to use what you have taught me for the spirits he serves, which can only be spirits of evil!"

"You are wrong, Zahia. Dagmar is not evil, he's a wounded man. Once he was an initiate, a shaman, but a terrible drama placed hatred in his heart.

He has tried to forget his suffering, thanks to his passion for horses, but it is still there. Without wanting to, your presence and the horror aroused by your enslavement have woken his old demons.

The roots of evil

It's not up to me to reveal what shattered his life, but you have to know that your destinies are similar, and he could not bear to relive, through you, his terrible trials.

Here in Siwa, Dagmar found uncouth people who serve a terrible god, and his knowledge of magic straightaway designated him as Great Priest.

When he calls upon Exu to invest him and incarnate himself in him, it is because he thinks that this will allow him to defend a just cause".

"But Exu is evil, isn't he, Mamina, how could he do good?"

"It's the god of slaves, Zahia, of those who have lost hope and any faith in good. Exu was born from their blood and their fears. It is men who create gods; they only exist when they feed them. When they cease to pray to them, they die. That is how things have always been, since the world came into being.

Exu incarnates evil. It is a reassuring power for those who have only known violence and ubservience. They invoke him to make the rain fall during droughts, or to stop the rain when it becomes devastating. To cure their illnesses and those of their cattle. To encourage the harvest. But sometimes also for less noble reasons: Greed. Cupidity. Vengeance.

Exu is a pagan divinity, like those that we invoke, child, it is only the vector of men's intentions. Because it is possible to kill in the name of God and heal in the name of the Devil".

"What you are saying is terrible, Mamina, must I understand that my dear spirits could also be used to do evil things?"

The barefoot princess

"Of course, Zahia, there are no evil forces: magic is innocent, it's the heart of men which are not. We have the gods we deserve!"

"But Mamina, the statue of this Exu grimaces, and it is surrounded by an evil aura?"

"That statue, Zahia, was sculpted by men to create fear. No doubt they thought that it would be more effective to represent evil than good! Do you remember those shamanistic ceremonies that you attended with me, and the masks that some of the officiants carried?"

"Yes, Mamina, some of them were quite frightening".

"Yet, Zahia , the Shaman certainly intended to heal ... only, you see, when man talks to the entities of heaven and Earth to save a sick soul, he feels so small that he believes he must seem menacing to assert his power ... then he feels he is dealing on an equal footing".

"It sounds as though you are defending these practices, Mamina, yet you were always appalled by those sorcerers who practiced bewitchment, whether it was for love or death";

"I'm not denying myself, child, I am just telling you that Dagmar allowed himself to be possessed to assuage his hatred, perhaps without the other participants knowing it. I'm not defending him either; I just understand the roots of his suffering. Unfortunately, I also know that by making these evil forces reappear, this man is in the process of losing his soul.

The roots of evil

Like you, Dagmar suffered from the activities of the Priest Gilles, and he is using this cult as the instrument of his vengeance.... and yours.

He is suffering, and you alone, Zahia, given time, can lead him to calm his anger and his thirst for vengeance."

"But how, Mamina, I'm so little?"

"You must recreate in him the emotion he has lost."

"What is emotion, Mamina?"

"Emotion, child, is the soil which makes souls flower."

"When I feel in my flesh the suffering of men, animals or even the plants I pick, is that emotion, Mamina?"

"No, that perception of the other is empathy, compassion. Sharing the other's emotion. A way of relieving part of his suffering. What I am talking to you about, Zahia, is that special vibration that only speaks to you alone: it is the spark that links each of us to the soul of the universe".

"How was Dagmar able to let that spark go out, Mamina?"

"By refusing everything that can nourish it: fine music, poetry, magic, love ..."

"But why would anyone give up all these fine things?"

"So as not to suffer any more, child."

Dagmar was betrayed, banished, and spoliated. They stole what was dearest to him in the world, and to protect himself and no longer feed that great wind of hatred that "devastates him, he refuses anything that makes his heart beat faster. He has made his soul a desert where only horses can find a rightful place."

119

"But how can I bring that emotion back to life in him, Mamina, when I know so little of life?"

"It's already happened, Zahia. The echo of your soul has resounded in the Dagmar's heart. The terrible act he committed is that of a man submerged by a wave of emotions that he is not yet capable of controlling. It is up to you to appease him, as you did with the wounded horse that was contorted with pain. You alone can teach this man to abandon himself, little by little, to gentleness."

"Will I be able to, Mamina?"

"You will find the way, Zahia, I'm sure of it, but for now, you must continue to have confidence in him and follow his teaching, as if you had forgotten all you have seen.

"I can assure you that Dagmar means you no harm and will never pervert your gift. He left you the choice of accepting or destroying that fetish, which was created as much for you as for him. That was a generous act because the entity he serves could turn against him. It was also a saving act, because it proves that the power he ascribes to Exu has not completely poisoned his soul."

"Thank you, Mamina, I feel somewhat relieved and even if I don't know how I am going to heal Dagmar, with the help of the spirits and you, I'm sure I will be able to find the way to his heart and his redemption."

The roots of evil

That night, despite Mamina's soothing words, I slept very badly. I saw again and again the scene that had so impressed me, and the ritual with the statuette. Early the next morning, the Lady of light came to me in a dream and said,

"If you wish to help Dagmar, Zahia, you must make a figure of him with the wax left over from producing your ointment. You must put a few of your master's hairs in it, taken from a brush in his bathroom. In that way, you will create a link between his soul and yours, and you will tell this wax doll everything that you are unable to say to him."

"But isn't that an evil act, a sort of bewitching?"

"No, Zahia, it's an act of love and peace, because, as your grandmother told you, what can be used to do evil can also be used to do good.

It is not yet in your power to make this man listen to reason, but with your pure heart you can quietly pull on the deepest strings of his heart.

It will take a long time, and use a lot of your energy, but I know that you will succeed.

However, you must respect the three essential rules of magic: to know, to dare, and to keep your peace.

Nobody, not even your friend Chavha, must know about this ritual. Be discrete, young Zahia, or your efforts will be in vain."

The barefoot princess

As soon as I awoke, I prepared Dagmar's breakfast with Chavha, but, no doubt exhausted by the shock of the ritual, the master had not come home.

While my friend listened to some music in our little bedroom, I told her I was going to withdraw to the laboratory to prepare my decoctions, then, discretely, I went back to Dagmar's apartment.

In fact, not without some apprehension, I went into his bedroom. The bed was still made. It reassured me a little. The master must certainly be sleeping somewhere in the old village of Chali.

In the adjacent bathroom, I took a few hairs from his hairbrush, as the Lady of light had told me.

When I when back into the bedroom, I noticed a photo on the bedside table, showing Dagmar with a young woman and an adolescent. He looked happy and displayed a smile I had never seen him show.

I was about to leave when I noticed his silhouette in the tall glass-fronted cupboard: he looked really furious. ...

"This time you'll not escape, Zahia," he said, get out of here and come and see me in the lounge in 10 minutes!" I feared the worst...

Dagmar turned me round with a rough gesture, and tore open the back of my gandura with his sword. Then he took hold of a whip and gave me a dozen lashes which whistled through the air like angry serpents.

The roots of evil

I was amazed, because it hurt far less than I had imagined. However, I could feel the blood running down my back, and then, suddenly, I collapsed on the floor, unconscious.

I woke up on my bed, in front of a panic-stricken Chavha who was bathing my temples with cold water. She removed my gandura and discovered the terrible "bites" of the whip.

"Are you in a lot of pain?"

I shook my head.

She cleaned the bloody wounds and I made a sign for her to give me the gauze compress. I thought I recognized a familiar smell: belladonna.

So that was it: Now I knew why it didn't hurt, despite the deep cuts. Dagmar had covered the lashes of his whip the juice of that plant, which is a powerful analgesic.

Now I was certain that the master of the horses did not have a heart of stone. And even if I had to blow as hard as the simoom, the little spark would one day become a pure blaze of joy.

Chavha took Mamina's balm out of the medicine bag and spread it in a thick coating on my wounds. As I had done for her, she did not cover the cuts immediately, because the balm must be left open to the air to take effect.

So I lay on my stomach for a while, still in a state of shock, nonetheless impressed by the adventure that linked me strangely to Dagmar.

The barefoot princess

My friend asked me why I had been punished, but I did not reply. She respected my silence without insisting.

After resting for a few hours, I felt better, and Chavha covered my lacerated back with compresses, held in place with adhesive surgical tape.

Then, from the pocket of the now useless gandura, I secretly removed Dagmar's hair that I had taken from his hairbrush, took out the spare gandura from the cupboard and put it on.

In fact, apart from the risks I had run and the punishment I had suffered, I was rather proud of myself. I had achieved my objective - my master's hair would weave links of love between us that would, I hoped, appease his sufferings.

I left my friend prepare dinner and returned to the plant shed, to prepare the wax figure according to the Lady of light's instructions.

However, when I saw Dagmar's face take shape under my fingers in the soft wax, I felt very uneasy. I had the feeling that I was violating his soul, and the fact that it was for his good did nothing to ease my conscience.

Was I not also playing at the sorcerer's apprentice? Had my dream betrayed me? "Help, Mamina, tell me if I am doing right?"

"Don't worry, child, you did what was right!"

"If you say so, Mamina, it must be true ..."

The roots of evil

For the two days after my punishment, I had no call from Dagmar. He even told Chavha that he did not wish to see me ... until further notice.

I took advantage of this to pursue my studies of Arabic, and while Chavha did the cleaning in the master's apartment, I isolated myself in the plant shed to talk to the wax figure, that I had hidden behind the pots, on the highest shelf, so that my friend would not discover it.

I didn't yet know which words of appeasement to say, but little by little, helped by the spirits and Mamina, deep in my heart I found the words that could touch the heart of Dagmar.

"I have confidence in you, master, I know how you have been wounded in your soul and - I'm so sorry that my own suffering has come to awaken your own. I don't know how to help you because I know nothing of your wounds, but I can tell you this, because I have proved it for myself, vengeance will not heal them. On the contrary, it's as if you poured acid to make each wound deeper.

Yes, that man deserves punishment, but the law of return exits, master. By staying what you are, a good man, all the forces will conspire to revenge you, without you having to dirty either your hands or your fine soul. The expiation of Father Gilles' faults will be terrible but it is not up to you to be the architect of it.

You heart is too full of hatred to leave room for hope, but believe your little Zahia, who knows how to talk to the spirits, the future has sweet and fine surprises in store for you. May the kiss that I leave on the place of your heart soften your grief and wipe out that hatred that prevents light to enter your soul!"

The little damp foal with his pale brown coat
stands on his thin legs,
Which are as unsure as the fingers of a new-born child

Ivan Skala

10

BIRTHS AND REBIRTHS

I had scarcely returned to my bedroom than the bell that connected me to Dagmar's apartment rung out.

Fortunately I had not yet undressed. I grabbed my medicine bag and ran to my master.

"Two mares have just broken their water," he said, "We have to act quickly: come with me!"

While we went to the stables, Dagmar explained to me that he had asked the grooms to get the four mares together in the same area, with plenty of space, ready to foal, so that I could help him efficiently and follow his instructions.

The two mares in labor were lying on their side and the feet of the foals were already visible in their membrane.

Dagmar took charge of the first and asked me to make sure, for mine, that one of the hooves was in front of the other, to facilitate the passage of the shoulders.

The barefoot princess

Everything seemed to be going smoothly for Dagmar's mare, but mine was having a difficult time. The foal was big and the delivery was difficult.

Instinctively, I pulled gently on the foal's feet, in time with the contractions, and Dagmar indicated to me that it was the right thing to do:

"Hold him, or the cord will break and as blood is still circulating through it the foal could have a hemorrhage, which could kill him. You'll have to manage on your own, I can't help you, the hooves of my foal are still in the mother's vulva and I must free it to avoid giving her lesions that could make her sterile."

So I did my best to prevent the foal from falling out onto the straw.

It was long and difficult but handling the fork had hardened my muscles, and after a dozen minutes or so the umbilical cord, deprived of blood, had stopped beating, and could be cut without danger for the foal. What a relief!

Meanwhile, Dagmar had freed the feet of his foal, but the foal wasn't moving and we were very worried.

So I rediscovered the gestures of my healer ancestors.

Births and rebirths

Very gently, I cleaned the foal's nostrils and blew into them several times, then splashed water in his ears. It worked at once - the foal began to breath, and so did I, because I could see professional approval in Dagmar's eyes, although he said nothing.

The master took the new-born foal by his hooves and turned it upside down, so that blood could flow to the brain. He was saved.

However, our task was not finished. Dagmar pointed to a large piece of cotton wool soaked in tincture of iodine that he had brought with him and placed in a gourd.

"Do as I do," he said, "Hold this disinfectant on the foal's umbilical scar for a few minutes."

I did so as best I could, and the foal relaxed, as did the mare, who tacitly delegated her power to us.

"Now we have to vaccinate them both," said Dagmar, "It can't wait until tomorrow because there is always the risk of infection."

He placed his knee on the neck of the first foal, and held its head so that the end of its nose pointed upwards.

"Hold his legs, Zahia, he mustn't be allowed to wriggle."

Dagmar gave the foal a sub-cutaneous injection and we repeated the procedure with the other foal.

Finally, we rubbed them both down with straw and helped to them to find their feet by passing our arms under their chests and holding their little tails up with the other hand.

The barefoot princess

Life had found its way again, and it only remained to let the mothers get to know their offspring.

With difficulty, we brought them unsteadily to their mothers to help them find the teats. We covered our fingers in milk and held them under their nostrils, pushing them gently towards the teats.

"You did a good job, Zahia," said Dagmar, "And, as all work deserves its reward, if you have a favor to ask me I shall be happy to satisfy it."

I hesitated, because I knew that what I was going to ask was very bold:

"Master, will you allow me to ride Medina, if only for a few minutes?"

"Medina!" he replied, astonished, "When?

Now?!"

"Yes master, now. Everybody is asleep and nobody could see me."

"Look, the horse has to be saddled, and I'm really very tired."

"No, master, I want to ride him bare-back, with no saddle, no bit and no stirrups .... just with a leading rein and reins."

"But that's impossible, Zahia, how could you climb onto his back without stirrups ? He's twice as high as you are !"

130

Births and rebirths

Dagmar could read the determination in my eyes, and as he knew that I was as stubborn as a mule, rather than trying to reason with me he went to get Medina and brought him to me.

From the way the horse rubbed himself against me, I knew he had recognized me. So I concentrated my thoughts to ask him what I was expecting of him.

Before Dagmar's dumbfounded eyes, the horse lay down, and then when he felt that I was properly settled on his back, he gently stood up.

After a slight touch of my heels on his sides, my marvelous pure-blood began to gallop, carrying me with him in a wild ride, identical to my dream in every respect.

In only a few minutes we reached the salt lake, which sparkled under the stars.

We turned round, and I saw Dagmar, perched on his black stallion.

"I followed you because I was afraid for your life, but you're amazing, you flew faster than the wind!

I know it's your first ride, and I didn't know that you had this gift too.... now I know what remains to be done."

And then I heard myself reply, in a voice as clear as spring water:

"Yes, Master. Thank you."

The wild gallop on this horse had given me back the words that exile had taken from my throat.

There is no secret that time does not reveal

Jean Racine

11

THE SECRET REVEALED

The weeks and months which followed were punctuated by an unchanging ritual. Each morning was devoted to the study of Arabic, and then of English, because for reasons that I did not grasp, Dagmar wanted me to learn the rudiments of that language too.

In the afternoon, after a short siesta, I went to my little laboratory, where I perfected the recipes for ointments, balms and elixirs recorded in Mamina's exercise book.

The shelves were now well stocked with phials and pots, containing remedies for humans, but above all for horses, because Dagmar had categorically forbidden me to treat the staff of the stud or the villagers.

And every morning, without fail, I spoke to the wax figure representing my master, and I had the pleasure of seeing him relax and become more human as the days passed.

The barefoot princess

Was it me that effected this change? It didn't matter, reality said I was right, and that delighted me. Dagmar even favored me sometimes with a smile that would have been unthinkable before.

No, I did not know if my ritual played a role in this transformation, and sometimes I even hoped that the change of mood was natural, because despite Mamina's encouragements, I still felt uneasy, acting in this way without my master knowing it.

In the evenings, when the servants and grooms had returned to their dormitories, we would leave together for a wild ride. We galloped through the dark night while our horses' hooves raised clouds of the hot desert sands.

The feeling of supreme happiness made me forget, for a moment, what I was and what I had been. It was as if I was in a dream. A dream that I would never have imagined in my poor life.

Dagmar taught me all the finer points of his art and while he now accepted willingly that I rode bareback he knew how much I enjoyed this direct bodily contact with Medina - he also required me to ride more classically, with saddle, bit and stirrups.

He taught me the *haute ecole* steps and invited me to dance with my horse as I had seen him do himself - in the most private and perfect complicity.

I quickly became an accomplished rider, combining speed, equestrian figures, vaulting and dressage.

Dagmar called me whenever a horse was unwell or simply excited. He never gave me any instructions, relying entirely on my healer's instinct.

The secret revealed

One evening, usually so direct, he asked me in an embarrassed manner which surprised me:

"Zahia, you are very young, and I have hesitated a long time before suggesting that you could help me with services. You have lived in the heart of the countryside, but have you already seen animals mating?"

"Yes master, and I found that as natural as to see bees pollinating flowers."

"You know how impatient the stallions are, and the mares are jumpy, at mating time. That's why European studs use artificial insemination. It avoids any risk of damaging the mares. But we aren't equipped for that in Siwa, and there are often accidents that make the mares unfit for reproduction.

Your gift would be invaluable to me for calming the stallions. But I don't want to shock you, or oblige you to do it. What do you think?"

"I should be happy to help you, master. It won't bother me at all."

So I assisted with several services, calming the frightened mares and controlling the ardor of the stallions, without hobbling them, which would have left indelible scars. Dagmar was very pleased with my help, and he often rewarded me with little gifts which touched and delighted me.

He gave me botanical books which completed the information Mamina had given me, bars of wax for my balms, lanoline extracted from sheep's' fat, and a set of pretty amber-colored pots with labels, so precious for noting the dates of my preparations, and a set of plant illustrations, with which I was able to identify the new plants that I found during our excursions.

The barefoot princess

He also showed me how to capture the soul of plants by distilling them to extract the essential oils. As well as my traditional remedies, this enabled me to make soap, hair lotions and various beauty products to soften the skin, the hands and the body, that delighted Chavha and me.

During this period nobody suspected my true identity, and except of course for Chavha and Dagmar, nobody knew that I had recovered my ability to speak.

Though I often thought about my family - often about my little sisters, hoping they wouldn't suffer the same fate as me - slowly the pain faded, and the little girl I had been grew into a woman.

For my 15th birthday, Dagmar gave me a very pretty dress, making it clear that I should never wear it outside the house. He also lent me a story book. I especially liked the tale of "Donkey Skin", with whom I identified immediately. When I slipped on my silky dress, it was as if I exchanged my donkey skin for dress the color of the sun or the moon.

I admired myself in the mirror, and played the coquette. I did not suffer from being disguised as a boy, but it gave me so much pleasure to feel myself a woman for a short while.

The secret revealed

Nevertheless, that lovely present was nothing compared with the news that Dagmar had for me a few days later.

"You are a real rider now, Zahia, and I'm proud of you. I've decided that you are ready to take part in the grand annual race, held each year for the princes, sheiks, emirs and sultans who come to compete against each other and test their qualities as horsemen."

"Master, do you really think I have any chance of winning?"

"I think so, Zahia because I've never seen a rider as fast as you."

"May I ride Medina?"

"Yes, you will ride him, because together you are one being. He obeys you implicitly. Do you know the prize for this race?"

"No, master".

"A pure blood horse that will be yours for ever, if you win." -

"Is it possible that Medina could belong to me one day? It would be too good to be true!"

"Yes, Zahia, but for that you have to deserve it."

"Will the owner of the stud accept that even if I win, one of his pure bloods could become the property of a slave?'"

"It's the law, Zahia, and if you have that chance I will ensure personally that it is respected."

The barefoot princess

The long-awaited day came, and I found myself in the lists with all the most eminent personalities in the Arabian states.

I was very intimidated, because though I had grown a lot, alongside the other riders I looked liked a flea on a stallion, and as I took my place on the starting line, I heard a few mocking comments from the other participants.

It made me feel very ill at ease.

Only Selim, Prince of Jahal, who had won the race two years running, looked with interest - and some indulgence - at this young lad who was going to race against him. I even detected a glow of admiration in his eyes ... for my rashness, no doubt.

Dagmar started the race, and I forgot everything but my communion with Medina. I didn't even notice that some competitors tried unfairly to cut my route to make me fall.

All I saw was the enthusiasm that fired the galloping horses. The flaming hooves and the sparkling horse shoes like a scarlet breath filling the air. The frenzy of the innumerable hooves that flung sand like gold dust. The sparks flew towards the future like a swarm of luminous arrows.

The frantic race drew me with it, and the foam from Medina's mane mixed with the glowing horde which crackled like a plume of fire under the red sun of the white desert.

The secret revealed

Closely followed by Prince Selim - the other competitors were already out of sight - I raced towards victory, several lengths ahead.

The first to congratulate me was Dagmar. He hugged me fiercely, for the first time ever, then Prince Selim came up to me and gave me a mighty slap on the back.

"Bravo, kid, you really deserved to win".

I was on a little cloud. Or rather, I was on another planet. It didn't matter much to me that I had one, but knowing that Dagmar was so proud and Medina was now my horse filled my heart with joy.

As for the owner of the stud, he showed himself to be a good loser, and whispered to me:

"Congratulations, little girl. Dagmar has trained you perfectly." And he added, with a slight smile that didn't entirely please me,

"It's true that he must have enjoyed it, because you have become a very pretty girl."

The feast continued with great libations, and lagmi, palm wine, flowed freely, but I retired early to avoid any indiscrete questions.

For me, the only thing that counted now was to take my horse home.

Dagmar had promised me that from now on Medina would be kept in a private box just next to that of his black stallion. So I could groom him and feed him myself, without having to meet the other grooms.

The barefoot princess

Nonetheless I was a little bit worried because a pure blood was an expensive luxury and, as a slave, I had no resources. I decided to open up my heart to my master about it.

"Don't worry, Zahia, your horse is in good health, and when there is enough for one, there's enough for two. Anyway, now you have proved yourself I am going to enter you for other races. Some of them have big money prizes. That way, if you win, you will be able to put the money by and use it to meet your own needs and those of your horse."

"It would be wonderful to become a fully-fledged rider, but I want to remain in your service, master, I owe you so much."

"You have already given me a lot, Zahia, and seeing you develop is the finest gift that you could give me."

Full of joy, I was completely unaware of the next trial that fate had in store for me...

❖❖❖

That night, I let Medina rest - he certainly deserved it - but I promised myself that the next day I would go for a long ride with him, by day this time, because from now on everybody knew me as Zahiel the winner, and while I wanted to remain discrete, there was no longer any point in hiding.

The following day at dawn, I saddled my horse and went to a place that never ceased to fill me with wonder since Dagmar had showed it to me: the temple of the oracle of Amon, the ram god.

The secret revealed

It is a magical place where Alexander the Great, Croesus and Hannibal came to consult the oracle. That was where I would go when my heart was heavy, to invoke my dear spirits and offer them cowries collected from the banks of the salt lake.

It was terribly hot, and there was never anybody around, I offered myself a refreshing stop in Cleopatra's Bath, a natural basin deep in the rocks, filled with sparkling water.

l had always been tempted to bath there but had never come without Dagmar, and this moment of solitude was sheer happiness: bathing practically naked. I removed my gandura and took off my trousers, and wearing only my muslin shirt I soaked myself with delight in the bubbling water. .

I did not know that behind a spiny hedge a man was watching, and when I got out of the bath my figure showed through the wet cloth, revealing my true identity.

❖❖❖

That very evening, Chavha told me that Dagmar wanted to see me as soon as possible. When I went to see him in the lounge, his face was expressionless and I could see both worry and anger in his eyes.

"You were very careless, Zahia. This is going to cause terrible changes in your life, and also in mine."

"Why, master?"

"Prince Selim saw you when you were taking your bath, and now he knows that his formidable rival is none other than a woman.

141

He came to see me, and told me without beating around the bush that he wants to buy you and take you with him."

"But why?!"

"You intrigued him, and certainly seduced him with your beauty. However, I told him how old you are, and he promised not to force himself on you, at least not before you become a real woman.

I know him well. He is a man of duty, and I know he would keep his word. But he is also obstinate, and won't tolerate any obstacle to his will. He has undertaken not to reveal your secret if I let you go.

So I spoke to him of your gift, and the reasons why I took an interest in you. I thought that would make him change his mind because Muslims don't like those who have powers, especially when it is a woman. It was a waste of time, in fact I would say your specialty amused him and only made him more determined."

"This child cannot live wear this disguise forever, she has to learn to become a complete woman," he told me. "In my palace I have a school where she could learn everything she lacks right now: poetry, music, flower arrangement ...

Zahia is too beautiful and too talented to remain a slave. I promise you, Dagmar, to make her a free woman, and perhaps my wife one day, if Allah allows it."

"What can I do, Zahia, that man has your life in his hands. You don't belong to me. I cannot stand in the way of his wishes, even if that pains me.

The secret revealed

"As for the master of the stud, he cannot intervene because he can refuse nothing to a man who buys several of his finest horses every year ..."

"Master, I am happy here. I don't want to be torn away once again from those I love and respect."

"It's the price of your carelessness, my child. Who knows, the Prince is young and handsome, and although he is a Muslim, he has studied law in Europe, and he is much more open-minded than most of the other emirs. Perhaps one day you will find with him the happiness you deserve."

"Is there really no other solution, master," I asked, distraught.

"No, Zahia, I admit that, at the risk of being thought depraved, I even considered telling him that you were my concubine ... but I have too much respect for you to sully your reputation like that. I also had the idea of marrying you in secret, to save you from this new exile."

"Why not do so, master, you know that I respect you and I would be faithful to you ... unto death!"

"Little Zahia, your confidence goes right to my heart, but I'm more than twice your age, and even if I were mad enough to forget it, there is a woman already in my heart - I will no doubt never see her again, but I refuse to betray her. For me you will always be the child I love, and I place my trust in life to make this sudden change which burdens you the promise of a better life."

In despair, I ran to my room where I cried my eyes out. I even thought of running away: but where to?!"

The barefoot princess

Prince Selim came to collect me the following day. I obtained his permission to bring Medina with me, which was some comfort.

After all, I told myself, Selim didn't seem to be unkind, and it had to be admitted that he was very attractive!

The Prince had bought three pure bloods from the stud, and the grooms installed them with Medina in a cattle truck on a thick bed of straw. Selim told me that I would travel in his jeep with him, but I refused outright:

I knew the difficulties of the track and I didn't want the horses to panic and suffer, so I demanded to travel with them, to calm them with my presence.

The Prince accepted, but he was clearly somewhat angry. Dagmar had warned me: he didn't like to be contradicted.

Dagmar said his goodbyes to me, and I saw that he had tears in his eyes. Why did he not want me? What was the secret that was eating into his soul?

I tried to hide my feelings, but I felt rejected once again and my tears flowed inside me as if from inexhaustible spring.

I asked Dagmar where we were going.

"To Saudi Arabia, Zahia, in an oasis close to the coast. You will cross the Red Sea by ferry."

I realized that there was little chance of us ever meeting again one day, and I clenched my fists very hard to avoid giving in to despair.

The secret revealed

Leaving Chavha was also a great wrench. I could have asked for my friend to accompany me, but for the past few months she had been seeing Abdul, a young groom, and I didn't wish to be an obstacle to a love affair that my intuition told me would soon lead to marriage.

With death in my soul I made my way towards my new destiny.

The slave draws his pride from his master's embers.

Saint Exupéry

12

THE ROYAL HAREM

Prince Selim's palace stood in the oasis of Jahal, close to the frontier with the Yemen, at about 60 miles from Jisan, the port on the coast where we disembarked.

It was smaller than I had imagined, and was not fortified like that of the masters of Siwa. When the horses and I got down from the cattle truck, I saw that the stables gave onto the outside.... the desert.

We went into a large hall that looked like a church, with its central nave. It led to a small saloon where the Prince's throne was placed.

The walls and ceilings were completely covered in frescos representing hunting scenes and wild feasts, filled with unclothed women.

The sumptuous room was connected by a door to baths like those of the Romans that I had seen in my school books at Mekele. Over them, a sky-colored dome displayed the signs of the zodiac.

The barefoot princess

"Look, child, that is the Great Bear. When it is clear in the sky, the harvest season has come.

That's the constellation of the Lion, it announces the rainy season, and when it shines less brightly than that of the Scorpion, we have to prepare for floods."

The entrance to the harem was in the second courtyard of the palace. It had a dozen rooms, scattered around confined courtyards and reached by long dark corridors.

A small saloon, which contained an immense bookcase, separated it from the royal harem, which only contained four bedrooms.

"That is where my future wives will live," the Prince said to me, "But for the present I am still a bachelor and so I have decided that you will reside in this wing of the palace.

My own apartments are in the private area, where my mother also lives. She manages the entire harem."

❖ ❖ ❖

The queen mother was a plump little woman whose eyes were as sharp as a falcon's. She received me with a certain coldness, and I felt that my presence was far from welcome in the royal harem.

"Zahia," she said to me, "Because of your youth the Prince asked me to grant you a special status. You will not live in the harem reserved for the women, not with the rest of the servants, chambermaids, cooks and matrons, but here, in the royal harem.

The royal harem

"It is an exceptional favor, and you must show that you are worthy of it. I hope that you will not be tempted to escape, because the desert is pitiless. You would be caught immediately and severely punished.

"Furthermore," she added, "the outside doors of the harem are guarded by soldiers, and any inclination to escape is pointless."

"So am I a captive, then, Highness?"

"No, you may go out sometimes - especially," she added, "if you show yourself to be less insolent - but you will always be closely watched. I have been told that you can read and write. You will be allowed to correspond with your family and friends, but your letters will be read before they are posted."

"Without wishing to offend you, Highness, why is the mail opened and read?"

"Because the Prince has great responsibilities and here in Jahal we do not want spies or women who have relationships with unsavory characters. It's the rule, and you must accept it."

After this scarcely affable, but eloquent, interview, when the door of the harem closed on me, I knew that despite the Prince's promises to make me a free woman, I was a prisoner again.

However, though my heart still held the radiant image of the simple but pretty room I had shared with Chavha, I could not contain my admiration as I discovered the suite that had been reserved for me. I had never seen so much luxury and refinement: it was royal!

A large four-poster bed, adorned with veils woven with golden threads, stood on a platform covered with an oriental carpet.

The barefoot princess

The ivory silk sheets just asked to be caressed. The damask cushions strewn over the bed and the two sofas were a discrete invitation to nonchalance and relaxation.

A toilet table, holding a marble basin, was surmounted with a cut-glass mirror with metal flowers entwined in delicate spirals.

A sideboard in dark wood carved like lace, carried a multitude of pots of cream for care of the face and body.

Perfume bottles stood next to accessories and jewels for the hair: brushes, combs, and barrettes, in gold, ivory and tortoiseshell.

In an adjacent alcove, separated from the bedroom by a curtain of multi-colored pearls, stood a huge copper bath.

A little table was covered with flasks containing rare flower essences. I recognized some familiar scents, but others were completely unknown to me.

When I opened the French windows in my bedroom, a little garden full of white, purple and tea-colored roses presented itself to my wondering eyes. They had the unforgettable scent of my wild Abyssinian roses.

In the midst of this flower-bed stood a fountain, a thin jet of water which murmured gently and seemed to converse with the birdsong that came from an immense bird cage. There were dozens of them fluttering and chirping in their golden cage.

At the end of the garden stood two tall palm trees, facing the wall of pink granite that bounded my domain.

The royal harem

Deep in contemplation, I did not hear the discrete knocking on my door. Two servant girls came into the room, begging pardon for their intrusion. They brought hot water to fill my bath and pour into it a shower of rose petals.

Despite my gestures of refusal, they removed my clothes, loosened the tight plaits that, under the turban, gave me the appearance of a boy, and covered my hair with a lotion to untangle the more easily.

Then they bathed me with a sea sponge, and massaged my hair and my body, aching from the journey, with perfumed oil.

When they saw that I my body hair had not been removed, they prepared strips of hot wax to remove my superfluous hair. I accepted them waxing my armpits and my legs, but when they wanted me to sacrifice my pubic fleece I refused categorically. This providential growth of hair allowed me to hide my intact intimacy: no question of touching it!

Confronted with my fierce obstinacy, the women abandoned the ceremony, but from their faces I could see very clearly that it was only postponed. They were going to make their report to the queen mother, I was sure of it.

They dried my hair with a device that blew hot air, brushed them for a long time and then dressed me in a gossamer tunic that emphasized my growing figure.

After they had gone, when I looked in the mirror, I thought I recognized the Lady of light, as she appeared to me in the Spirit tree, which disconcerted me.

The barefoot princess

A servant girl brought me a light meal in my room, with refined and delicious delicacies, but all this attention for me did nothing to appease my sorrow.

However, tired by the journey, and perhaps also by overindulgence in palm wine, I slept like a baby after savoring in my heart these words of Mamina's:

"I'm here, little one. You have surely not reached the end of your troubles, but it's certainly not chance that has brought you here: you have a task to perform. The spirits will guide you."

❖❖❖

I did not see Prince Selim for several days. I didn't miss him, but I needed to speak to him as quickly as possible. I could not leave the compound to see Medina, and it filled me with despair, even though I knew he was cared for, because here, as at Siwa, horses were certainly better treated than the women!

Fortunately, I had brought with me the wax figure of Dagmar, and it comforted me to be able to speak to it. I had the impression that he was there, near to me.

The queen mother came to see me, and seemed satisfied with my new appearance.

"After all," she said, inspecting me from head to foot, "Perhaps my son is less mad than he appeared. It remains to be seen if your soul is as beautiful as the promises of your body..."

Then she told me to join the other women: an invitation which did not delight me, and seemed much like an order.

152

The royal harem

Stretched idly on soft couches, a dozen women looked at me with suspicious curiosity.

They were certainly assessing my chances of replacing them in the heart of the Prince, for it was obvious that this was his livestock!

They were dressed in richly embroidered silks, decorated with gold and precious stones. Some of them were savoring candies; while others drank coffee or tea that they prepared in a large copper samovar, with precise but lazy gestures. Yet others smoked opium pipes, stretched out languidly on rich cushions.

Their long dark perfumed hair floated on their shoulders, enhanced with russet highlights, due no doubt to the henna that Chavha liked so much. None of them thought to bid me welcome, except one, who rose and came towards me.

"My name is Shoga, and I'm Jordanian" she said. "You're new. What is your name?"

"My name is Zahia and I come from Egypt."

"I know you live in the royal harem, are you the Prince's new favorite, or perhaps even his future wife ... you are so lovely?"

"No, Shoga, the Prince just insisted that I should be isolated, no doubt so that they can keep watch on me more easily, as I'm only 15 ..."

The young woman seemed reassured: I was not a serious competitor, at least for the time being...

The barefoot princess

"You are certainly very young, Zahia, and you have nothing to fear - or hope for," she added with a smile, "the Prince is only interested in real women with full figures, or those who know how to amuse him by their wit, their musical talents or their skills as storytellers.

However, when you have grown and gained experience, the women here will have cause to worry.... you should be wary of them because some of them can be formidable enemies ...."

"In any case, you don't seem to be worried, nor jealous, Shoga?"

"And for good reason," she replied, I'm in love with a young man named Arkham, who works in the stables. He's a groom, and also the master's chauffeur from time to time. He's not an ordinary employee: he's here against his will, like me, and no doubt like you.

We very much hope to find a way to marry one day. Of course it's only a dream, but for me the idea of becoming Prince Selim's concubine is a nightmare."

"Why do you trust me so, Shoga, when you scarcely know me?"

"Because a little voice tells me you won't betray me. You know, they think I'm a bit special here. I sometimes talk to the spirits and foresee the future. Islam forbids divination but my "gift" amuses the others and they often ask me throw my stones on the ground and tell them the meaning of the patterns they make.

"What do they ask you, Shoga, their future here seems already settled?"

The royal harem

"All their questions are about the Prince. Will he choose them for the night? Will they be raised to the rank of favorites? Will he marry them? Will he give them a child?

Oh! You can be sure that as soon as you have left, they will ask me about you and your chances to conquer Selim's heart..."

"But are they all in love with him then?"

"How naive you are, Zahia, what these women are looking for above all is power, that is why they are dangerous...

"Now we are all going to the hammam: would you like to come with us?"

I had no idea what a hammam was, but I agreed, so as not to admit ignorance.

My first impression, when I entered the room covered with blue mosaics, was of suffocating steam and heavy perfumes that made me nauseous.

The women were seated on sofas covered in cushions and rich carpets, while behind them stood their slaves, but without the marks of rank normally shown by their dress, because they were all in the most natural state possible, in other words, completely naked.

I immediately took a step back, because I did not wish to undress in front of them. My refusal intrigued Shoga and the other women, but they put it down to young modesty or perhaps they thought that I was having a period.

I left the hammam quickly, because my tunic was sticking to my skin and I had difficulty in breathing.

155

The barefoot princess

I quickly went to take refuge in my room, and above all, take a deep breath of fresh air from the rose garden.

A tray was already waiting for me, and seeing the copious, rich dishes on it, I wondered if the queen mother - who had an eye on everything - was not trying to feed me like a goose to make me as plump as she was.

I contented myself with some chicken breast that I isolated from its sauce, some fruit. It was enough, because here the body could also be changed by lack of exercise.

I also skipped the palm wine. To put together my escape plans I was going to need a clear head.

In the afternoon I attended a lesson in flower arrangement, which seemed rather unreal to me, because for me plants are nature's finery, or the partners in my treatments, but I had never thought they could be used for anything else.

I had to admit that the bouquets were very decorative, but as I cut the flower stems I couldn't prevent myself from talking to their spirit, asking their pardon for this outrage.

I only murmured my word, but despite myself my lips moved, and now the women looked at me, nudging each other and laughing discretely. Without knowing it, I had just reassured them. They thought that I was mad, like Shoga, and so I had no chance with the Prince, who only liked normal women.

Then I took part in a music lesson, where I learn to pluck the strings of a sort of lyre that resembled that of Mamina. I took interest in it despite myself, in homage to my grandmother.

The royal harem

When I returned to my room, I found the door next to mine half-open, and had a glimpse of a veiled woman whom I had not seen with the others. I went to ask Shoga if she knew who my mysterious neighbor was.

At first she didn't understand who I was talking about, and then her expression darkened:

"You must her avoid that woman, Zahia, in fact I don't understand how they could have given you a room next to hers. She's a leper, and nobody should go near her."

"A leper? Are you sure, Shoga ? It's a terrible disease but I know that today there are ways of curing it.

Why does the Prince keep her in the royal harem? It's even more dangerous, for her as well as for us."

"Perhaps she is of his family, or perhaps she has committed a serious fault and this detention is her punishment," replied the young girl.

"No fault can justify being abandoned like that, Shoga; I want to be clear in my mind about this."

"Do as you wish, Zahia, but take care, because if she contaminates you, I could no longer see you, and believe me, I would be very sorry about that."

"Do you know her name?"

"Yes, her name is Leila and she never goes out, except for a walk in the garden when night has fallen."

The barefoot princess

Intrigued by this mysterious woman, that very evening I removed my slippers and climbed the palm tree, with my feet flat against the scaly trunk, as I did when I was little.

I watched out for the recluse to come out, and called out to her from my perch high in the tree.

"Leila, Leila, I'm your neighbor, I would like to speak to you. I have something important to tell you. Please open your door to me!"

The young woman was surprised. She had difficulty in seeing where I was, but finally located me by the sound of my voice, and looked up. Believing herself to be alone, she had removed her veil, and the moonlight lit her face.

She was a woman of about forty, and would have been beautiful but for her face - which seemed familiar to me - damaged by a disease which, it seemed to me, was more like herpes or psoriasis than leprosy, though when I was with Mamina I had never had to treat people stricken by that scourge.

"You shouldn't come near me," she said to me, "I am contagious".

"That doesn't bother me. I'm used to treating people, and I promise to keep my distance. I just want to talk to you."

By dint of insisting, I persuaded Leila to accept, and open her door. I joined her in her room.

"My name is Zahia and I'm Ethiopian."

Those words must have been inspired by the spirits, for I had not revealed my origins to anyone.

The royal harem

Although my Arabic was sometimes hesitant, the others assumed it was due to the Siwa dialect, which is different to the Arabic spoken here. To my surprise, Leila replied in my language.

"So am I. I lived for a long time in Mekele before going up to the capital."

Driven by an irresistible impulse, I wanted to hug Leila, but she pushed me firmly back:

"No, I understand your emotion at discovering that we are both from back home, but you must not touch me, you promised."

"I saw your face by the light of the moon, Leila, and I know you do not have leprosy. My grandmother was a healer, and I learned a great deal from her. I can assure you that the skin disease you have is not contagious even if I touch your scars. It's a very common skin disease and can be treated very easily. If you will trust me, I think I can even cure you."

"Thank you, Zahia, but I don't wish it. This disgrace protects me from the Prince. It allows me to reject his advances."

"Why, Leila? The other women seem only to want that, and you are beautiful enough to be his favorite."

"I belong to another man," she told me, "I would sooner die than betray him."

"Those are worthy sentiments, Leila, but you will not always be a prisoner here. If you let your disease get worse, the day when you find your lover again, it will be too late, it will have become chronic."

The barefoot princess

"I can see that you are new, Zahia, and above all, full of illusions. I have been here, hoping, for years. I now know that to be captive in a harem is never temporary. As soon as the door closes on you, you are there until your death."

"But the Prince is not a monster. He has studied in the West, perhaps all you need to do is speak to him."

"I've tried, Zahia, but it's a waste of time. That man knows how to appear civilized when he travels outside of this kingdom, but as soon as he returns, when he is in his stronghold, he complies with his traditions and his religion again. Here, Selim is considered to be a living god, and when he buys a woman or receives one as a gift, even if he does not make her his concubine, she must remain in the harem all her life. It's the law, and nobody can escape it."

"Is there no way of escape?"

"Believe me, I have thought about it, but I'm not alone. The Prince also holds my son, Arkham, who is his squire and his chauffeur. Despite my pleading, I have never seen him since I have been here. He must be a man now.....I had hoped to convince the Prince to let us meet, if only for a few moments. But to do that, I must speak to him, and Selim is convinced that I have leprosy, so he avoids any contact with me and forbids anyone to enter my room."

"But, your door is not shut."

"Oh yes it is ... by fear!

"The servants just leave a tray at the door of my room, and jugs of water for my toilet, but nobody ever visits me, except for you, young and foolhardy that you are."

The royal harem

"Doesn't this life of a recluse weigh on you, Leila?"

"No, I have my memories, and the books that the Prince has delivered to me, and this radio that keeps me in touch with what is happening in the world. That is enough for me."

"Were you sold as a slave?"

"Not exactly. I'm a sort of .... war trophy. My husband was a member of the Derg, a group that stood up against Haile Selassie's despotic rule. He was denounced for money by a despicable priest, who said he was one of our friends, just before the Negus was deposed. All his property was confiscated. Fortunately partisans helped him to escape the day before he should have been executed. I don't even know if he is still alive."

"But why did he not take you with him?"

"We were separated. I was already in prison in Addis Ababa, with my son, and we rotted there for two years."

"How did you go from that prison to Prince Selim's harem?"

"One day, there was an amnesty. My son and I were thrown out of our jail, but we had nothing left. Our bank account had been frozen, and the fine house, where we lived so happily, had been requisitioned. As for our friends, those who had not been shot had fled the country. I had to beg to keep us alive. One day one of the people in the Prince's entourage gave me alms at the door of a church. He thought I was beautiful and brought me back as a gift for his master. I cold have resisted but he promised me a better life, and above all, not to separate me from my child: I accepted, for Arkham.

The barefoot princess

The Prince was scarcely twenty years old. I was ten years older and it was my maturity that appealed to him. I was very different from the women he was usually with. I could read and write, I am a musician and I know horses well. Despite the age difference, Selim very quickly decided to make me his wife. My disease arrived just in time to dissuade him.

The queen mother, far from approving the marriage, because she was afraid of my influence on her son, shouted to the rooftops that I had leprosy. Selim was too young, and respected his mother too much, to try to have me examined and treated. A leper: they must be shut up, or they are sent away to rot in a leper colony! He was not so cruel.

It was his promise to look after Arkham and give him a job that kept me going.

As for me, Zahia, I welcomed this disease as a gift from heaven. Whether he is alive or not, my husband is still alive in my heart and the idea of belonging to another, even if he is young rich and a prince, was unbearable for me."

"I understand, Leila, but have you any idea what sparked off your disease?

"Shock and fear, I think. Unless it was malnutrition or a virus contracted in the street when I was begging. You know, there effects are not immediate and they often wake up when emotions are too strong.

Today my sole consolation is to know that Arkham is happy. I know he can satisfy his passion for horses. You see, he always lived among them. My husband had a stud farm and loved them passionately."

The royal harem

Leila's last words had opened a breach in my memory. Now I knew where I had seen that woman: on the photo in Dagmar's room. But I did not wish to give her unfounded joy before being sure.

"Before coming here, Leila, I served as a slave in a stud far on Siwa oasis. I was saved and educated by an admirable man whose name was Dagmar ...."

"Dagmar, my husband was also called Dagmar," said Leila; I could see that she made no connection with the master of the horses.

"Leila," I said to her, "I saw a photo of you and your child in my master's bedroom. I'm now certain that he is the husband you are looking for, and believe me, he neither has ever forgotten you. He bears your absence like a cross."

"Zahia, is it possible that fate has brought us together like this?"

"Only last night, my grandmother told me that there was a reason for my presence here, and now I know what it is.

Yes, Leila, Dagmar is alive and I promise you that I will find a way to save us and reunite the three of you."

Any power is weak, unless it is united

Jean de La Fontaine

13

THE SACRED UNION

After that first meeting with Leila, which moved us both deeply, we decided to give each other time to think to prepare our plan.

Above all, we must not be surprised together by the queen mother or servant girl, which would ruin our hopes of escape.

However, before leaving the young woman, I had to convince her to begin her treatment, that very day.

"Dagmar must find you as lovely as when he last saw you, and Arkham must be proud of his mother."

I went to fetch Mamina's balm from my medicine bag and said to her, "You must rub this into your scars every day and only put on your veil when it has penetrated your skin completely."

165

The barefoot princess

We also decided on a code: three knocks on the wall separating our rooms meant that the way was free and we could meet without risk.

It now seemed essential for me to contact Arkham, and I would need Shoga's help for that. I would need to take her into my confidence. I met the young girl in the great saloon.

"Would you come to my room this evening, because I can't speak to you with the other women around?"

Shoga hesitated, but after all, nothing in the rules forbade us to have friends, nor to have tea together. That evening, the young girl knocked on my door. I told her what I had discovered:

"Leila is not suffering from leprosy. She is the mother of Arkham, the man you love - but I think you already know that - what you don't know is that she is the wife of my master at Siwa: Dagmar. We are going to escape, Shoga, but for that we need your help."

"May I come with you?" she asked, timidly.

"Of course, there is no question of leaving you here!"

"I'm entirely at your disposal Zahia. You know how much we Arkham and I love each other, and even if there is little chance of succeeding: well, it's worth trying."

"I have to get in touch with Arkham; you already have, so you must tell me how it can be done."

"Every evening I have to take him the mail that the harem women send to their families.

The sacred union

"Then Arkham posts it in the village with the master's jeep."

"So he isn't deprived of his freedom, like us?"

"No, he is free, and the Prince has every confidence in him."

"Do you think that it would be dangerous to give him a letter from me?"

"Not if I tell him that the letter is from his mother. It's important, because Arkham venerates Selim, who brought him up like his own son, and he could be tempted to denounce our escape project, thinking he was doing right."

"It's obviously a big risk to take; he hasn't seen his mother for years. He perhaps only has a vague memory of her".

"I don't think so. During our brief meetings he often speaks of her and asks me for news of her. Like everyone here, he thinks she has an incurable disease, and that clearly makes him very unhappy. He also talks about his father, and I can feel that he has certainly not forgotten him, even if he believes he is dead."

"Thank you for that precious information, Shoga. I will write that letter, and I'm counting on you to give it to him."

❖ ❖ ❖

It took me a long time to write the letter, because my Arabic - written, especially - was still faltering, and I doubted if Arkham remembered his mother tongue. Here is what I wrote to him:

The barefoot princess

"My name is Zahia. I am Ethiopian, but I worked for more than two years in an Egyptian stud farm. Not long ago, Prince Selim bought me, and I live in the royal harem.

My room is just next to that of Leila, your mother, and I have been able to make contact with her.

Let me reassure you straight away, Arkham, contrary to the rumor, your mother is not a leper; she is only suffering from an easily-treatable skin disease, which will soon be no more than a bad memory. I am a healer, and so I don't say that lightly.

While talking to your mother, I found not only that we came from the same region, but that I was in direct contact with your father.

Yes, Dagmar is alive. He is living in Siwa oasis, in Egypt, and not a day passes without him thinking of you, though since his exile he has had no news of you.

I know you are profoundly attached to Prince Selim, who treats you kindly, but I know you also love Shoga. She has become my friend, and we are planning to escape together to return to Ethiopia and warn your father so he may join you there.

Your mother follows the international news on her radio and knows that you will not run any risks in returning home.

She has friends there who can help her, and we are only 60 miles or so from Jisan, where we could find a boat to take us across the Red Sea, but for that we need your help.

The sacred union

I know you drive Prince Selim's jeep, and, having done it myself, I also know that it is possible to climb over the wall of the garden next to my room. The wall gives directly onto the outside, and so all you would have to do is to wait for us with the jeep at the foot of the wall one night (so we won't be seen), and then take us to Jisan.

Your mother has a few jewels that she could barter with a fisherman to take us across.

Arkham, I know that we would be running a great risk, but I hope that to be reunited with your parents and with Shoga is your dearest wish. So we are all counting on you, because without you nothing will be possible!

Shoga informed me that the Prince travels regularly to Mecca for business. He often stays several days, and goes by his private plane rather than by car. So it seems to me that the best solution is to take advantage of one of his absences to escape. As soon as one of us knows that Selim is going to be away, they must tell Shoga. She will be the link when she brings you the mail, and we can set the rendezvous.

I will leave your mother to complete this letter.

Best wishes,
ZAHIA

My darling son,

I never thought I would see you again and certainly not to have news of your dear father. Young Zahia has given me new hope of holding both of you in my arms one day.

The barefoot princess

I know that you are perfectly at home here, and that Prince Selim treats you well. However, deep in my heart, I hope that you still remember the happy days when we were together, all three of us.

I also hope that you have enough love for Shoga to live with her in that great happiness that you deserve.

Will you take the risk of escaping with us, my dear child? That is my dearest wish and my last hope.

Your loving mother,
LEILA

The evening I gave the letter to Shoga, Prince Selim summoned me to his apartments.

I went dressed as a boy, as in Siwa, hoping I wouldn't meet the queen mother on the way.

"Why have you put on your old clothes, Zahia, I've been told you are very pretty dressed as a girl?"

"Because I hoped, Excellency, that you would take me to see Medina. I miss him so very much. And perhaps even go for a ride in your company. But I don't know if girls are allowed to go into the stables and ride horses...."

"I understand, Zahia, but I am the master here. I often receive lady visitors from Europe, who wear riding dress to accompany me in the desert.

The sacred union

"I will have one made for you. You will be more at ease, and I will be delighted to go riding with you."

Prince Selim went out for a few minutes and returned with a type of riding outfit I had never seen before: riding breeches, black velvet silks and a strange-looking piece of head-gear.

"It's a riding hat, Zahia; it protects your head if you fall. You are too good a rider for that but it will hide your long hair, and you will look like a young boy, as you did when I first met you, and nobody will be able to say anything against it."

Selim saw that I was reluctant to undress in front of him, which made him smile. He pointed to a screen, behind which I could change without being seen.

In passing, I noticed a table set for two, with candles and a bottle of that palm wine that went to my head so quickly.

Had my request distracted the Prince from his original intentions? And if I had arrived dressed like the beautiful harem women, would he have kept his word to respect me, as he had promised Dagmar?

No doubt I would never know, but I had to admit that this very attractive man disturbed me, despite myself, and it was with a touch of regret that I showed myself to him in my riding clothes : clothes which seemed perfectly ridiculous to me...

"That suits you very well, Zahia, but it's a good thing that night has fallen, because you have become quite shapely now, and it would be difficult to take you for a young boy."

The barefoot princess

I felt my cheeks become red, which didn't escape the Prince's notice...

"Well, you are really becoming a woman, and I'm not sure I will be able to resist you for much longer. Come now, Zahia, don't worry, I'm not going to eat you - at least, not yet! Come along, let's go the stables.

I'm sure Medina is just as impatient to see you as you are to see him."

When I saw my horse I could see that he had been treated like a prince. His coat shone, and his airy, spacious box was perfectly clean. The groom had even plaited his tail and mane so that he wouldn't be bothered by the heat.

I asked Selim, who had just saddled his horse - a magnificent grey pure blood - if it had any objection if I rode bareback? It surprised him, but he accepted, curious to see how I would manage.

Medina remembered our old gestures and a lay down on his side before lifting me on his back like a feather. Selim was very impressed.

We galloped for a long time, a moment of eternity. I slowed Medina from time to time, to allow Selim to pass me. I thought it important not to upset the Prince's pride.

"Have you lost your touch, young girl, or are you pretending?"

I blushed once more, but the night was there to hide my emotion. Was I so transparent, or did Selim have gifts of clairvoyance like Dagmar?!

The sacred union

"That ride was wonderful, Zahia," the Prince said, "I enjoyed it immensely, because no other rider can match you.

If you wish, we will go out every evening, except for the next two days, because I have to go to Mecca on business, and I won't be back in the palace at night."

That evening, I knew that this was our chance and that it was certainly the last time I would see Medina - which hurt me terribly - but also Prince Selim. Strangely, that thought did not leave me indifferent.

14

THE ROAD TO FREEDOM

My ride with the Prince prevented me from contacting Shoga after she had given my letter to Arkham, so I had no idea what the young man had decided. The following day, I met her in the patio, and she told me her lover was wild with joy and ready to help us.

She also told me - as I already knew - that the Prince would be away that night and the rendezvous with Arkham was set for four in the morning.

"Why so late, Shoga?"

"The fishermen go to sea at six am, if we arrive earlier we will be noticed and it will be dangerous."

Back in my room, I knocked three times on the wall, and Leila opened her door to me. I told her that the great day had come: that night, we would escape.

"What must I do?" she asked.

"Get together everything you possess, Leila, because we will need it to pay the fisherman who will take us across in his boat."

"That's not a problem. Selim was very generous when I arrived at the palace, and I have a casket filled with precious jewelry."

"You should also do as I have, and plait the sheets from your bed in to a long rope. There is no palm tree on the other side of the wall, and it's too high to jump without breaking a leg."

"But how am I going to climb to the top of a palm tree? I'm not as young as you, and I'm certainly not as agile."

"I will climb first with Shoga and I will tie the rope we have made to the top of the tree to lake your climb easier. When you are with us at the top, and we see Arkham's jeep, we will throw the rope over the other side and all we will have to do is slide down it."

"Is there no risk of the queen mother catching us? She is insomniac and does rounds of inspection at night."

"Don't worry, Leila, I have a plan."

"Have you thought that we are going to land in Eritrea? Do you know that part of the country is currently disturbed by a guerilla war against the Red Negus? Isn't it risky?"

"I know nothing about politics, Leila, but everything is risky. I thought about going via the Yemen but it appears that the situation is even more disturbed there.

It is only about ten miles from the port of Massoua, where I hope the fisherman will be willing to take us, to Addigrat, where there is a direct train for Addis Ababa. We can walk it, and with any luck, we will avoid the guerrillas."

"So you don't intend to stop at Mekele to see your family?"

The road to freedom

"No, Leila, and believe me, it hurts me a lot to go so near without stopping, but I think we will be in a better position to organize ourselves from the capital, and above all contact Dagmar.

Added to which, I have nothing to give my family. For now, I'm just a fleeing slave. My presence might even be dangerous for them."

"I promise you, if we reach the end of the journey and I find my dear Dagmar again, I will give you my help just as you have, so generously, for us."

"Thank you, Leila, but don't let's get overcome by emotion. All our energy must be concentrated on the success of our escape. By the way, I have a request to make."

"Yes, Zahia, what is it?"

"Don't ever say 'if' again. We are going to succeed, Leila, and negative thoughts won't help us. You have to believe in yourself to the end, so that hope is transformed into our final freedom."

"You talk like a shaman! Your grandmother must be proud of you ..."

For the journey, it would be a good thing to dress as Shoga and I will, in a gandura and turban, to avoid us being noticed."

"But I don't have either."

The barefoot princess

"But I do. I Egypt, Dagmar obliged me to dress as a boy when I looked after the horses. I brought the clothes with me as a souvenir, and I will give you one, we are about the same size. Bring warm clothing too, because the night is cold, and our sea crossing might be very trying for you."

"Look, Zahia," said Leila, lifting her veil, "My scars have almost disappeared: your ointment is truly miraculous."

"The miracle, Leila, is that we met, and whatever gods you pray to, you should thank them."

"I'm a Coptic Christian as you are, Zahia, but my husband was animist and a shaman, and I also pray to the spirits sometimes."

"I was baptized too, my mother was Christian, but it was my grandmother's beliefs that gave strength to my soul. She was a shaman too, and she bequeathed me all her powers. However, she taught me that any belief is good when it is inspired by love and tolerance."

"What should I take with me for our escape, Zahia?"

"Nothing, Leila, except for the jewels and the addresses of the people who can help us in Ethiopia. We must not be too loaded because the journey is going to be long and difficult.

I will only take my medicine bag and the few treasures that Mamina left me."

I took care to tell Leila that I was also taking my wax figure: it was the indispensable link to connect me to Dagmar, but the very instant when my master found his son and wife again, I would drop into a stream. They alone, henceforth, would have the right to have mastery over his soul.

The road to freedom

"Let's get on with it, Leila. I'm going to settle the last details with Shoga, and tonight we shall be free."

❖ ❖ ❖

Before returning to my room, I asked a servant girl:

"Bring me a hot infusion: I'm not feeling very well."

She hurried to obey, and I prepared a strong decoction of poppy seeds and hops, with orange flowers to lessen the bitterness.

The dinner tray arrived shortly after. I scarcely touched it, but put aside some fruit and candies for the journey, and the carafe of palm wine, to which I added my decoction.

When the queen mother came by, as she did each evening to inspect her troops, I invited her to take an aperitif with me.

She was astonished, for our relations were far from friendly, but she didn't say no: the bottle was her secret weakness!

I knew she would forget her insomnia and surprise visits, that night.

Then I hurriedly prepared my rope, which I was unable to do so before, to avoid arousing my guest's suspicions at the sight of the ravaged bed.

The barefoot princess

When I returned to Leila, our two ropes end to end were about twelve feet long, which seemed adequate.

We tied them together and tested their resistance. They seemed well capable of doing the job. Shoga came in at three am, wearing her gandura, and Leila put hers on. If we weren't examined too closely we looked like three boys, and despite the tension of the moment, it amused us.

I climbed up first, tied on the rope and after some failed attempts due to the slippery silk of the sheets, Shoga and Leila managed to climb to the top.

Arkham arrived punctually at exactly four o'clock, and after I had lashed the rope firmly, we let ourselves slide down, at breakneck speed. The kindly moon hid behind a cloud to help our flight.

The moving reunion between Arkham and Leila brought tears to our eyes, but this was no time for emotion. The jeep took off, with its lights out, and less than two hours later we had reached Jisan.

The youth, who spoke better Arabic than his mother or I did, negotiated the crossing with a fisherman, who wasn't interested in Leila's jewels: he wanted the jeep.

Arkham gave him the keys of the vehicle, somewhat reluctantly, for he had his principles:

"This jeep belongs to Prince Selim," he said, "As soon as I can, I will pay him its price."

We embarked on a felucca, a tiny cockleshell with a large triangular sail. We didn't dare breathe freely until we were in the open sea. At last!

The road to freedom

The crossing was uncomfortable but we were so exhausted, as much by our joy as by our excitement, that we managed to doze off, despite the discomfort of the felucca.

It was also very cold, and Leila hugged me, leaving Arkham to do the same with Shoga, and he didn't stint himself!

Some souls go to the absolute
as water goes to the sea

Henry de Montherlant

15

THE COUNTRY I COME FROM

We would confide in each other later. For now, I savored this exceptional moment, for I had been deprived of the tenderness of a mother for a long time.

When we arrived at Massaoua, we thanked the fisherman, and for good measure, Leila gave him a ruby ring, asking him to speak to nobody about our night-time escapade.

Would he keep the secret? We could not know, but now that I had returned to my own country I felt invulnerable.

We flew off towards the Danakil desert, where we had the luck to meet some Bedouin, who offered us two camels for the ride to Addigrat, in exchange for Leila's pearl necklace.

I found the price excessive, but I could see that my friend was tired, and above all, the jewels Selim had given her were burning her fingers. She was in a hurry to get rid of them.

The barefoot princess

In less than an hour we had reached our goal, but night had already fallen and there would be no train before the following morning. We were starving, and above all, we needed a good night's rest.

Arkham and Shoga had collected a nice sum of money, but Dirhams were not accepted here and we had to dig into Leila's jewels again.

We stopped at a little country inn and bartered a diamond-studded watch for some rooms and a good meal.

The injera pancakes garnished with a chicken stew seemed tastier than any of the harem's refined delicacies.

What supreme elation! We were free and everything had a new flavor for us, and we were delighted even with the bedrooms and their rough straw-filled mattresses.

The following morning, after a cup of the Ethiopian coffee that we had missed so much, we went to the station.

The train was a small local affair, but we didn't care. On the contrary, it gave us the chance to talk and get to know Arkham better, who was so much like his father.

We arrived at Addis Ababa in the afternoon, where Arkham and Shoga converted their Dirhams into Birrs in a foreign exchange office near the station.

"Now we are rich, "said Leila, "Tonight we shall sleep at the Taytu Hotel. It's the most modern in the capital, each bedroom has ensuite bathrooms, and we certainly could use them, but above all, they have direct phone lines, which will I will need to contact the people who can help us."

The country I come from

I assumed that we would all sleep together, but Leila - even dressed incongruously as a boy - had become once again what she had never really ceased to be : a great lady.

No question of arguing: she decided that we should each have our own room with its private bathroom.

We were received somewhat coldly at the hotel reception: our dress left a lot to be desired in an establishment of this class. But as we paid cash, the faces at the desk quickly became more amiable.

We each took possession of our room, and what first attracted my attention were neither the view, nor the huge welcoming bed, but the immense bath, promising relaxation and well-being.

Lying in the hot, perfumed water, I dosed off, and if Shoga had not knocked enthusiastically on my door, I would probably have stayed there all night. I dragged on a large toweling dressing-gown and opened the door to her.

"Well now, lazy-bones, I'm sure you were asleep. Your eyes are still all puffy with sleep. Get dressed quickly; Leila is waiting for us in her room: she has things to tell us."

"My problem, Shoga, is that I all have to wear are these sweaty, sandy clothes ..."

The barefoot princess

"We are all in the same boat, Zahia, except for Leila who couldn't resist bringing one of her dresses, despite your advice .... too bad for her if she is ashamed of us!"

But Leila had good news for us, and that was all that mattered to her.

"We are going to visit a couple of Dagmar's friends tomorrow morning," she told us, 'They are very influential people. I explained our situation to them, and don't worry, they won't be offended by your clothes."

❖❖❖

Our hosts lived in a sumptuous private house near the University, the former palace of Haile Selassie. They welcomed us warmly, saying,

"I'm Radia and this is my husband Aghali. We would prefer you to call us by our given names: it will be friendlier."

Before even listening to our story, Radia led us to a dressing-room, full of clothes for men and women.

"Choose whatever you like," she said, "the bathroom is just next door and you can change while we prepare a snack."

When we returned to the large dining room, we looked human again. We were worthy of Leila and her sumptuous green silk dress.

"This is Zahia, our guardian angel. Without her we wouldn't be here. My son Arkham, whom you knew when he was little, and his fiancée," she said, indicating Shoga.

The country I come from

The young Jordanian was pink with pleasure. She felt that Leila had adopted her. Arkham took her hand so that she would understand that he approved of the title his mother had attributed to her.

After lunch, Leila recounted our saga and our incredible meeting to her friends.

"So Dagmar is alive!" they said, and I felt that their joy was perfectly sincere.

"Yes, but he doesn't yet know that we too are alive, and free."

"But the Siwa stud is one of the most famous breeding farms for Egyptian horses," said - Radia, "It must be on the phone, we must let him know ..."

I interrupted her:

"Yes, the owners have the phone, but there isn't one in Dagmar's house."

"That doesn't matter, they can tell him."

"Certainly, but nobody must know that it is we who are calling, because the master of the stud is a personal friend of the Prince, and if he learns who we are, he will probably warn Selim."

"I've an idea," said Aghali, "I can call Dagmar and pretend to be a breeder who wishes to purchase some horses. He's shrewd enough to understand."

"What will you tell him?" asked Leila.

"I won't speak of you, nor of Zahia, I will just tell him that he must come to Ethiopia urgently. I will inform him that his property is no longer sequestrated but is in danger of being auctioned off, because here everybody believes him to be dead."

The barefoot princess

"But do you think he will come?" I asked, "Siwa is a long way and he has so many responsibilities."

"Zahia, the stud owner's love of profit is well known, and Dagmar comes here to conclude a big sale of horses, I think he will be the first to offer him his limousine..."

I shuddered. Just thinking about the black limousine that took me away from my family made me feel ill. But it was an excellent idea, and I was sure that if it was properly executed, these people who loved each other would finally be reunited, for ever and only for the best.

"There is no point in waiting," said Aghali, "You have all suffered too much already - I'm going to call him at once."

Everything went perfectly. Dagmar, who had recognized his friend, assured him that he was alone in the room and could speak freely.

Aghali outlined his plan, explained what he should say to the stud owner, and the urgent reasons for his presence. He didn't reveal our secret: he had understood perfectly that we wanted it to be a complete surprise.

Dagmar declared that he would arrive in less than a week, after informing his master and delegating his authority to Abdul, the groom he had trained and who was now, I learned later, Chavha's husband.

The country I come from

Throughout the conversation between the two men, Leila had her ear glued to the earpiece.

The voice of the man she loved resounded in her heart like a song of joy, and tears flowed from her eyes in an unrestrained stream.

Traveler, traveler, accept your return
You have no more room for new faces

Jules Supervielle

16

THE LAW OF RETURN

Three days later Dagmar phoned his friends to tell them that he would arrive in Addis Ababa the following day.

We decided on a strategy. Our hosts would retire to their bedroom, as would Leila, Arkham and Shoga. I would open the door alone to the master and prepare him for his meeting with his wife and son.

The long-awaited day arrived. Dagmar rang the doorbell...

"Zahia! What joy to see you again! I missed you so much, my sweet", he said, hugging me tightly, "But what miracle brought you here?!"

"I escaped from Prince Selim's harem".

"From his harem! What are you saying, Zahia?

Selim never told me he possessed a harem. I didn't think that barbaric custom still existed. Did he at least treat you decently, as he promised me, my child?"

191

"Yes, don't worry, I was even treated with great respect, but that isn't the real reason for my escape."

"I fear the worst, Zahia, you are so impulsive!"

"In fact, master, I didn't escape alone ..."

"Well that's an aggravating circumstance: the Prince must be mad with rage. What did you do? Who did you persuade to come with you?"

"Do you remember the day when you whipped me because I had gone into your bedroom?"

"Yes, Zahia, but I did not punish you for your intrusion, but for what you had gone to get ..."

I was disconcerted. Was it possible that once again Dagmar had read my thoughts? Did he know about the wax figure?

"Don't get flustered, Zahia, I know that everything you did was to cure me of the errors of my ways. I heard all the words you addressed to me, here in my heart ... and the kiss you gave to my image melted the ice of indifference and the fire of hatred that was devastating my soul."

Overcome with an emotion that made me blush and my voice tremble, I managed to go on:

"That day, I saw a photo in you bedroom, a photo of you with a woman and a child, and you looked so happy."

The law of return

"Yes, it's true, but alas, that is no more than a memory!"

"Memories are made to be revived, master."

"Do you really think so, child?"

"I'm certain of it."

At that very moment, Leila, who could wait no longer, came into the room, followed by Arkham.

Dagmar could not believe his eyes: in a fraction of a second, his memories suddenly became real: it was wonderful! He rushed to take his dear wife and son into his arms.

Nailed to the spot by emotion, I managed to tear myself away, and reluctantly withdrew into the bedroom with Shoga. That exquisitely precious moment was theirs alone, and they had so many things to tell each other. So many lost caresses and kisses; so many years of misery and solitude to erase.

A few hours later, Radia came to find us, and we all congregated in the dining room.

"Zahia", said the master to me, "You have just given us back our lost happiness. I forbid you to call me "master" henceforth. You have untied the bonds of slavery, and today you belong to no-one but yourself."

Dagmar sensed the feeling of abandonment that made me reel...

"You will never again feel rejected, my child, you have just found a family. We will be able to care for you as you deserve, and our dearest wish is to see you blossom like a lobelia flower.

The barefoot princess

It's not easy to learn to be free, but we'll help you, and when you have rebuilt yourself you will be able to become mistress of your destiny. When that day comes we will open our hands to let you accomplish what must be."

Those who love truly, my child, are like the wise man that meets a lost little girl, takes her hand to place her on the right road, and then lets her go without trying to retain her... they are the bow, and you are the arrow.

"In the days to come, "added Dagmar, "I will get my things organized and decide what the future means for us all. But first, I am going to take you to your family, because you too must be reunited with them and put and end to your suffering.

You will only be able to grow when you have evacuated that feeling of rejection that is still tearing your soul apart. I don't want a little Zahia with a limping heart. It is an illusion to think you can forget, and we can only distance ourselves from the past when we are at peace inside ourselves.

If everything goes as I hope, Leila and I plan to sell our property and build a stud farm together in the south of France.

I have been thinking about it for a long time, and I have been offered some land there, but without the marvelous gift that you have just given us, such a project would have been merely an escape: that is why I never took it further.

The law of return

So in a few days I will come to fetch you in your village and we hope very much that you will agree to come with us on this great adventure. I also intend to bring Chavha and Abdul, her husband, who has become the image of myself. We will build the future together."

Please accept, my child: one day you will come back to the Horn of Africa, but meanwhile you have other missions to accomplish. And please understand that wherever you may be, I will always be close to you, because the spirits and I have no other land than that of your heart.

"Master - please allow me to call you that this last time - I will be very happy to come with you. I love this country. I love my family, but I have had too many painful experiences here. I know that the best thing for me is to distance myself, and above all, to live this new departure with you."

"I see that Mamina has spoken to you, Zahia ... my thanks to her."

❖ ❖ ❖

The journey in the limo with Dagmar was a moment of pure joy. I was able to tell him all the details of our adventure, of which he only knew the main points, and he spoke to me of his projects, and of the lovely plot of land at Grimaud, in the Maures massif, where we were going to build a model stud farm together.

"Dagmar," I said to him, "you are going to have to return to Siwa to speak to the owner, do you think he will let you leave without any difficulties, as well as Chavha and Abdul?"

The barefoot princess

"Certainly, Zahia, it's in his interest to do so: I'm going to buy a dozen of his finest horses to begin our breeding farm. I have the means to do so now, and I can advise him about the people he can rely on to replace me."

"How will we take the horses to France, it's so far away?"

"By plane, Zahia, we'll send them by cattle truck to Cairo, and from there that will be put on a plane to France."

I thought of Medina, and how much I was going to miss him, and my face suddenly fell.

"You will see him again one day, I'm sure of it, and he won't forget you any more than I forgot Leila and Arkham. Horses have even better memories than humans.

But look, we are nearly at your village - and there's a rather pretty river: don't you have something to give it?"

"Yes, master."

I took the wax figure from my medicine bag, and ran to give it to the spirits of the water....

"Undines, my friends, take great care of my master. May all the love I bear him join that of those who are dear to him, to wipe away his hurts for ever. May the beneficial water of serenity flow over his soul!"

❖ ❖ ❖

When we arrived in my little hamlet near to Mekele, the villagers recognized the black limo, even though four years had passed.

The law of return

All my friends were there - they were men and women now - and they ran behind the car shouting,

"Zahia, Zahia, Zahia has come back!"

We arrived in front of the hut: my mother had heard the echo of the cries in the murmur of the wind:

"Zahia, Zahia, Zahia has come back!"

She was on the doorstep, so thin, so small, so bent by the weight of years. I felt she had shrunk.

She ran towards me:

"Zahia, my little one, I thought I would leave this world without ever seeing you again. What joy!"

The simple words fell in a cascade from her lips, dried by a too-long silence.

"Just after you left, I learnt that Father Gilles was no more than a slave merchant. Every day since then, I have been eaten up by remorse. Will you ever forgive me, daughter?"

Faced with so much distress, contrition and sincere humility, I was completely overcome: I had come to demand explanations, to show my anger and my grief, and almost despite myself, nothing but honeyed words could escape from my heart.

"I don't hold it against you, mother. Thanks to Dagmar," I said, introducing my master, "Far from being treated as a slave, I was shown great kindness. He taught me his knowledge of horses, which was a great comfort to me. I suffered from your absence, but surely we all have to leave the nest one day?"

The barefoot princess

"Is this man your husband, Zahia?"

"No, mother, he is my master. He is Ethiopian, like us, and he has a wife and son whom he loves."

"So you are not married, Zahia?"

"No, mother, and I don't wish it."

So it had not taken long for my little mother to recover her aplomb, her inquisitive tone and her judgments which so made me suffer in the old days when she used to condemn my relationship to Mamina.

Was I wrong to feel sorry for her? Was I wrong to wish to spare her feelings?

"Your sisters are younger, and yet they are both married. Isn't our role as women to accept the domination of men and give them children?"

"Mother, you have the right to believe that, but I have another idea of life. For me, to serve only one man is to ignore all the others.

The man I will love - and that will happen one day, be sure of it - will never submit me to his will. He must look in the same direction with me, and together we will share and attain the aims we will have set for ourselves."

The arrival of my sisters and all the people of the village spared mother the need to reply, and so much the better, for the least reference to Mamina and her "detrimental influence" would have led me to pack my bags and leave immediately with Dagmar.

The law of return

They all stood round me, just as when I left, and in their eyes I could see admiration and tenderness, but also a certain embarrassment, tinted with repentance.

My sister Mira fell into my arms, weeping for joy, then she introduced me to her husband Adal, the very same who had given me my pretty agate marble so long ago.

Then it was the turn of Jena, the youngest, who kissed me and introduced her husband Said, the brother of Donna, the little girl who had allowed me to try on her new shoes.

One after the other, they all came to touch me, hug me, and ask me a thousand questions.

"How lovely you are!" said Lila - my friend the traitor, who had revealed my hiding place in the spirit tree:

"You see, I told you when you left us: it was for your own good. Today you wear a princess's dress and shoes, like ladies."

"Do you really think that fine clothes have more value than the loss of one's country and the people one loves, Lila?"

The young girl was visibly shaken, and I could feel that she was about to cry.

"Don't worry," I whispered in her ear, hugging her close, "I was happy there."

Lila looked happier, and she said a quiet "Thank you," that said much about the secret pangs of conscience she had suffered during my long years of exile.

"Are you going to stay with us, Zahia?"

The barefoot princess

"No, only for a few days, and then I am leaving with Dagmar and his family, to look after the horses, as I did at Siwa."

After sharing a glass of tella, millet beer, with us, Dagmar signaled discretely to me, so as not to disturb my reunion, that he was going back to Addis Ababa and would return to fetch me within a fortnight.

"Enjoy yourself with your family and friends, Zahia, and say hello to Mamina for me - I'm sure you will go and find her soon in the spirit tree."

Before I could react, he slipped an envelope full of bank bills into my hand.

"It's for your family. You were tactful enough not to speak to them about your enslavement or your escape from the harem, and it seems natural to me that the big-hearted little princess you have become can spoil them a little."

Dagmar could see that I was hesitating, and he added:

"This money is the wages you should have earned at the stud farm, Zahia. I would have paid you myself if I had been able to. Today, I can. So you owe me nothing."

❖ ❖ ❖

Night was already falling on the village, and yet nobody felt like leaving. I felt a little twinge of sadness at the thought that my departure would probably leave less trace in their memory than this glorious return...

The law of return

"Child, have you seen how the windscreen wipers of your father's car have the same swaying movement as the long neck of the pink flamingos when they swallow those little shrimps that give them their pretty pink color?

Well now, when you are plagued by black thoughts, imagine these little mechanical arms in your mind, sweeping away the rain. Right, left ... right left ... and your mind will become as clear as spring water again."

I took my new brother-in-law to one side:

"Here are a few bank bills, Adal, I noticed you have a car. I should like you to go into Mekele and buy enough food for a meal for us all this evening.

Here's a list with enough provisions for tomorrow. Don't forget the tella and bottles of lemonade for the children.

I would also like you to buy a portable radio: tonight, we're going to dance and have a party."

"This is a lot of money, Zahia: are you sure it isn't more than you can afford?"

"No, Adal, these are my savings from my wages at Siwa, and it makes me happy to be able to share them with you."

The young man returned shortly after with bags filled with food. My mother, my sisters and I got to work.

We prepared a large quantity of injera pancakes while mother concocted a chicken stew with green peppers and garlic, and tibs, delicious slices of sautéed lamb.

The barefoot princess

I could feel that mother was worried about this profusion of food, because we usually only ate meat for big feasts.

"Zahia, are sure there isn't too much?"

"We will be over thirty to eat, Mother, and emotions create an appetite ..."

"Don't forget the berberay !" Jena interjected, "the men love it!"

"You're right, little sister," added Mira, "But it's better to keep it separate so that everyone can take as much as he wants. It's too spicy for me and it makes the children cough."

While we were busy near the pan, the men made some chairs and a table from a plank and some logs, where we laid out the injera pancakes, big gourds full of fruit, and the sparkling drinks.

The littlest ones had gone to collect dry wood, and soon a huge bonfire reached towards the heavens like a prayer.

The music from the radio invited us to furious dances, punctuated by noisy crackling as the spirits of the fire accompanied our dancing to show their pleasure.

We feasted until far into the night when, exhausted but happy, I let myself fall onto my straw mattress, still damp from the recent floods. I was eleven years again, and only one person was missing: my grandmother. The next day I would go and see the spirit tree, I was sure I would find you there, Mamina.

"Yes my love, I'm counting on it."

17

THE RITE OF PASSAGE

The track across the savanna seemed very long. How could I have run so far once, with my little legs?

Finally, there before me was my fine master-tree! Still sturdy, its ghostly branches carried a few new buds that were just waiting to open.

I had pulled on my old tunic, so as not to damage the fine dress Rania had given me, and taken off my shoes, to feel the familiar burning soil of my land beneath my feet.

Before climbing my old friend, I took from my bag a dozen cowries that I had collected at Siwa, near the salt lake.

Quite naturally the old song fell from my lips, while I consecrated my shells with the sign that Mamina had taught me.

I chose the finest as a gift for my tree. It had waited so long...

The barefoot princess

I climbed easily up to the hiding place where the cowries were, and I saw that the little pile had grown. Who among my friends or family could have made these offerings?

Later, I learnt that it was Lila who used to come to perpetuate the rite, and to pray for my return.

A bird had made a nest near the shells, but was not there - by discretion, no doubt - leaving four little white eggs, which waited neatly for it to return. Life had found its way.

I slipped inside the narrow opening. It was more difficult than the previous time, but this place was mine. The master-tree knew it ... it seemed to me that the trunk was expanding, as if to receive me and protect me.

Suddenly the dear voice was raised in the silence:

"I'm here, my child, but this time it's not to comfort you: I know you are happy.

I simply want to hail your return. It's good that you have returned along the path to wipe away your wounds, without condemning your people.

However, while it was necessary to repair what was done, you must not go over your past. And it would be a mistake to stay here, even though I know you are thinking about it...

This time, Zahia, nobody is forcing you. You are free, and you must go forward to reach your true goal. France will only be a stepping-stone: your life still has surprises in store for you.

But never forget that you are the guardian of a unique gift.

The rite of passage

You are a shaman above all, and your vocation is to heal and enlighten.

Your sufferings were a necessary evil, so that you might better understand and help those who suffer in the same way. Follow your route, Zahia, but don't let yourself fall asleep in untroubled happiness. The way is difficult, but it alone will bring you true joy."

"I won't forget your words, Mamina, and I also know that if I lose myself, you will be there to call me to order.

But I need this period of rest that Dagmar has given me, to calm down a little.

You see, that man, about whom I sometimes had doubts, and would probably have rejected without your advice, is today my own personal master-tree. He is of our race, Mamina. He knows that he is my strength but that he is not my goal. So, when the time comes, he won't hold me back."

"You have certainly grown up, child. In a few years you will resemble the Lady of light that appeared before you in this very place. You carry her in you: it only remains to make her exist."

I put my cowry shell down near the birds nest and offered the spirits the little slippers given me by Dagmar.

"Spirits of the tree, these are my most precious possessions. They enabled me to keep standing when my limbs could no longer bear me, to find my dignity when I was a mere slave, and to meet a fine soul who reconciled me with life. Please help me to find my path and ensure that henceforth, that of Dagmar is nothing but peace and love."

The barefoot princess

In the days that followed, I went to visit all the people who were dear to me. Thanks to Dagmar's generosity, I was able to improve my sisters' their daily life, by giving them what they most lacked.

I asked Adal to take me to Mekele, and since the village had been supplied with electricity since my departure, we bought two television sets and two washing machines, which greatly impressed Jena and Mira.

Selma, the healer, who had been unable to come to the feast the previous night because she was helping with a villager's confinement, came to see me. I gave her Mamina's precious exercise book, for I knew it by heart and it could be of no further use to me, while I had a premonition that the village was going to need the enlightened knowledge of a wise woman, in the absence of a shaman.

I gave Lila a silken dress and the pretty pair of shoes she had dreamed of for so long. I thanked her for her offerings to the master-tree and asked her firmly not to reveal the cowry hiding place.

"Zahia, will you allow me to go there sometimes to meditate?" my friend asked, "I will feel less alone when you have gone to your distant country."

"Yes, Lila, but in secret. That tree is a magical place, and it must be treated with respect."

The Sunday following my arrival I asked mother if Father Gilles still held services at the church.

"No", she said, "He died in a fire not long after we learnt of his activities."

The rite of passage

"When did that happen, mother?"

"A little over two years ago, Zahia, there was a fire one night in the presbytery, and he was burnt alive. Nobody knows how it started."

My heart missed a beat. Was it possible that Dagmar's ritual had succeeded? Or worse still, had my burning the statuette - a gesture that I thought would save him - played a role in that terrible death?

"Stop tormenting yourself, child. The only causes of this accident are the man's cupidity and impure conscience.

We are shamans, Zahia, and our role is neither to turn the other cheek nor to forgive offence.

We are the crucible of invisible Forces, and even if you and Dagmar had activated them, one by vengeance and the other by love, these Forces would have consumed the soul and body of Father Gilles sooner or later, without your intervention.

Now, if you feel guilt in your heart, don't let it devour your soul, go and find the new priest and ask for absolution.

The fact that you were baptized makes you a link in a chain dedicated to this foreign god, which may not be as good as our spirits, but it's no worse than an other!"

"Who replaced Father Gilles, mother?"

A young priest from Cairo. Father Akar.

"I will go to church with you," I told her.

The barefoot princess

When I met Akar, I gave him an image that had never left me - that of his Christ.

"I am Zahia, who replaced you at Siwa, to look after the sheep. This belongs to you, and I wanted to give it back to you.

Bless me father!"

❖❖❖

I had hoped that this journey to the sources of my childhood would erase the rift: but it was not to be so.

I understood that this separation had been a rite of passage and it was impossible to retrace my steps.

Exutory words were pointless: my going had made me dumb, and my return obliged me to be silent.

I knew vaguely that for my mother and me these few days constituted a farewell: she was already on the threshold of a release, for which only her God would require a price.

My departure was the only possible liberation. The scar thus inflicted would fade with time, but its mark would remain written forever in my flesh.

❖❖❖

When Dagmar came to collect me, I took my mother in my arms. I assured her that I had not suffered from her abandonment of me and so I had nothing to pardon her for, because she had acted for my own good. The pale smile that lit up her face was the reward for my lie.

My child, my sister, think of the sweetness
Of going to live there together...

Charles Baudelaire

18

THE LAND OF THE MOORS

On the way, Dagmar updated me about his personal affairs.

"I've been able to sell some of my property, Zahia, and buy the plot of land I told you about. Abdul and Arkham have been there for the past week, and they are preparing for our arrival."

"When shall we leave, master?"

Dagmar made a little negative gesture with his hand, and apologetically, I corrected myself:

"When shall we leave, Dagmar?" and I added, "Pardon me, but it will difficult, because for me, you are still the master ... of my emotions."

"Skilful recovery, Zahia," he said with a smile, "and I certainly appreciate it, but next time that you address me in that way I shall be obliged to give you a spanking, so I hope you still have your balm with you !

And to answer your question, this evening we shall sleep at our friends' house in Addis Ababa. We leave tomorrow for France: Leila, my sweet wife, Shoga, my future daughter-in-law, and Chavha, your friend, who is waiting for you with great impatience."

"Just think of it, Zahia: four women just for me. I shall have to dress in western clothes or the passengers in the plane will think I am traveling with my harem!"

"And the horses?"

"We will collect them at Nice airport a week from now, when we have built comfortable boxes for them.

You will see, Zahia, they are exquisite."

"We won't arrive in Addis Ababa before this evening, Dagmar, and I won't be able to look for some decent clothes."

"Don't worry about that. My friend Rania has had the time to do some shopping with Leila and your two friends while I was in Siwa.

Your clothes are ready, already in the suitcases - except for your traveling outfits. The four of you will look like a group of trendy little French girls."

"I can see you've thought of everything, Dagmar, but where will we live at Grimaud?"

"The men have rented a little farm, near to our future stud farm. they've also bought a caravan so that we can take turns at keeping an eye on the horses, so as not to leave them alone in the fields. I'm told that there's a gypsy camp not far away, and while I have the greatest respect for travelers, our cultures are not the same, and there is no point in tempting the devil!"

The land of the moors

My reunion with Chavha was very moving. My friend was literally swimming in happiness, and while her veneration for me touched me, it embarrassed me somewhat. I tried to moderate her attitude, but she said to me:

"Zahia, but for you I would still be the whipping-girl servant in the Siwa kitchens.

But for you, I would never have lived happily in Dagmar's house, or even met Abdul, my beloved husband.

But for you, I wouldn't be about to live this exciting adventure that is awaiting us in France.

You have brought magic into my life, and even if I am older than you, you will always be my model, the big sister I always wanted to have."

"So you don't have any family here, Chavha?"

"No, all my family perished in the great flood of 1977. I spent five hours and more clinging to the trunk of the tree I had taken refuge in. It's a miracle I am still alive.

After the disaster, an association that helped the homeless found me a servant's job at Siwa, and the second miracle was meeting you, Zahia."

"This is no time to get sentimental, girls," interrupted Shoga, "come and see the outfits that we have prepared for the journey..."

Three western trouser suits waited for us, on hangers: we couldn't wait to try them on. They were pearl grey, the color of horses' coats, set off with white blouses.

The barefoot princess

That surprised me somewhat: even my gandura seemed more feminine.

"You'll have to get used to it, "said Chavha, "I've been looking through these fashion magazines, and these clothes are very smart. In France, women all wear trousers made of blue cloth that are called jeans, and also very tiny shorts and even miniskirts that reveal their legs!"

I tried my clothes on, and the girls did the same, so that I wouldn't be the only one.

"Look at us in the mirror, "said Shoga, "aren't we cute enough to eat?!"

"But we are missing something," said Chavha, reaching into the cupboard and taking out three pairs of varnished high-heeled pumps.

"I could never walk anywhere with those, " I said, "I've never worn such high pointed shoes in my life!"

"Well, you'll have to learn, honey," said Chavha, "we've been practicing for a week already. Leila taught us to walk with books on our heads to give us straight backs and an elegant bearing."

After a few clumsy attempts, I had to admit that these clothes, so different than my usual attire, set off my figure very nicely.

"Now we must take care of our hair," said the others, "Say good-bye to sensible little plaits. We are all going to have a "blow-dry" to smooth our hair, and then we'll tie them with one of these pretty barrettes that Radia gave us. It's called a ... pony tail: you must admit it's appropriate!"

The land of the moors

The night was short. Everything seemed to excite us: wearing new clothes, traveling by plane, discovering France, our new home, and for Shoga and Chavha, finding their men again.

Dawn found us waiting on the tarmac, impatient to climb into the big white bird.

None of us dared to admit their fear, but when my friends fastened their seat-belts, I could see uneasiness in their eyes.

Dagmar and Leila relaxed the atmosphere by calling us their "little schoolgirls". Our uniform could certainly cause confusion...

Everything in the flight enchanted us: our Horn of Africa that shrunk as we watched it, the huts and people who looked like ants, the clouds that veiled us, only to melt under our feet ... I even expected to touch the stars, or perhaps God, if he existed....

And there were the drinks and meals we were served on trays like princesses, and all those people, whose clothes, though strange, were now like ours. I glanced at Dagmar and Leila. My master was wearing an impeccable three-piece suit, a white shirt and a striped tie. Leila wore a suit similar to ours, but with a skirt.

"She couldn't bring herself to wear trousers," said Shoga, "it will take her a while to get used to the idea."

The plane began to descend, swooped down and we landed at Roissy airport, near Paris, from where we had to take another plane for Nice.

The barefoot princess

In less than an hour, scarcely long enough to fasten and unfasten our seat-belts, we had arrived.

I thought of the horses: they would certainly suffer less from this mode of transport than on our hellish journey from Siwa to Saudi Arabia.

Arkham and Abdul were waiting for us at the airport with an open-topped jeep.

"Tie a scarf over your hair, ladies," they said, "the mistral is blowing and you'll not want to arrive looking like scarecrows."

Leila had thought of everything. She took four scarves from her traveling bag and we knotted them around our necks like the peasants do back home.

After a high speed ride along the expressway - that frightened us a little - we took a little winding road among vineyards and finally arrived at Grimaud. Before going to look at the horse paddock, we stopped in the spacious farm, which was surrounded by a large flower garden, where we would be living from then on.

"I'll show you your rooms, ladies," said Arkham, "they aren't furnished yet but tomorrow is Sunday and nearby at Jas des Roberts there is a huge flea market where you will certainly find all you need. Meanwhile we have installed inflatable mattresses and hooks to hang your clothes."

When we shared out the rooms, there was a certain amount of wavering: the married couples would obviously room together, but it was more of a problem for Shoga and Arkham, especially with the parents there...

The land of the moors

Leila took Dagmar aside, and although the master of the horses dragged his feet - he had his principles - he soon understood that those two had already jumped the gun and it would be hypocritical to separate them.

So as a result I had my own room, with a superb view of the chateau of Grimaud, whose ruins already struck me as propitious place to evoke the spirits.

Apart from two large shared bathrooms, each room had its own small bathroom, and I predicted that mine would be used more for the preparation of my herbs than for my ablutions.

The lounge-kitchen was immense, with a fireplace made from dressed stone, and all modern comfort.

We sat around the large farm table to refresh ourselves with the jugs of lemonade that Abdul had prepared. This man was definitely a jewel!

"Before going to the stud farm, ladies," said, Dagmar, "I advise you to put on more sporting clothes, because the land is still uncultivated and you might get dirty."

So Chavha, Shoga and I tried on jeans for the first time. Frankly I felt a little ashamed, because it showed off my figure in a way that I found indecent, so despite the heat, I pulled a big sweater over my cotton t-shirt, which nearly reached down to my knees.

When we met up, we all burst out laughing, including Leila, because we were all dressed the same way.

"You're going to die of heat!" Dagmar told us.

"That's better than dying of shame!" retorted Leila. "Leave us a little time to get used to these clothes, will you? Anyway, yours fits you ... like a glove!"

Dagmar certainly looked superb, in a tight-fitting jean and a white singlet that set off his muscles to perfection.

He may have been nearly fifty, but he was a very attractive man, and despite myself I blushed, for his clothes reminded me of a certain ritual ceremony in which he was bare-chested.

"Look, even our little Zahia seems to find you to her taste," joked Leila.

Then she added, "Don't be embarrassed my love, I'm not jealous but rather proud that such a pretty girl appreciates my husband's charms."

Words were unnecessary for Dagmar. He knew which image had surfaced from the past, and with a friendly tap on my shoulder he brought me gently back to the present.

❖ ❖ ❖

What can I say about the paddock? It was immense, and quite free of any sort of building. I found it difficult to imagine that a week later it would be ready to receive the pure bloods.

"Yes my friends, "said Arkham," We are going to have to roll our sleeves up. Tomorrow we'll go to Jas des Roberts to get our furniture, but from Monday morning we'll start at dawn.

A team of gardeners will be here to turn over the land and plant the meadow, and planks and logs will be delivered. So we'll build the boxes together."

The land of the moors

Before returning to the farm, I went off to inspect the little caravan where we would take our turn at watching over the horses. It was a real doll's house, all decorated in pink like our room in Siwa.

"Will I be allowed to sleep in it, Dagmar?"

"Of course, Zahia, I have complete confidence in you. But won't you feel lonely in this vast empty plain?"

"Never with the horses!"

"Listen, this place is not very sure and you know how precious our horses are, so tomorrow we'll go together to a dog kennels at Plan de La Tour and you will choose a little companion to protect you when you are alone."

"Is it really necessary?"

"Yes, Zahia, because when the dog is not on guard near you, he will be at the farm to warn us of any undesirable visitors.

You could even take him with you when you go to collect herbs. And then," he added, "until you find the ideal companion, you'll feel less alone".

Wonderful Dagmar, who was always one step ahead of even my most secret wishes.

Yes, I had always dreamt of a little bundle of fur that would cuddle up with me to chase away the night's shadows. A living cuddly toy, which would calm me and reassure me, like the teddy bear I never had...

The barefoot princess

On the way back we stopped at Cogolin to make a few purchases for dinner. While the men sat down to an aniseed drink to discuss the organization for the coming days, Leila said to us:

"Before doing our shopping, we'll go to the bookshop and buy a collection of local recipes, to prepare a surprise for the men."

Then we sat down on a café terrace to look through the beautifully illustrated book, and conspire.

We decided on a pesto soup and stuffed vegetables which already made our mouths water. The local specialty, a Tropezian tart, was going to complete the meal, washed down as it should be with a rosé from the Var region.

Like good housewives Chavha and Shoga prepared a list, taking care to copy down the ingredients from the book, because not a single one of us - except for Dagmar - spoke any French.

The purchases in the Petit Casino next to the café were not made easily. We were often obliged to show the book to the sales girl to make ourselves understood.

When we returned to our companions we still had bright eyes from laughing our heads off.

❖ ❖ ❖

The meal kept its promises, and so did the rosé. I had never drunk any before, and I was soon a little bit tipsy. The men left us to prepare everything, but what surprised and touched me was that after dinner, they ordered us to go and rest: they would take care of everything.

The land of the moors

They cleared the table, cleaned up and did the dishes, and Dagmar was not the last to give a hand.

I was enchanted by this family life where everybody cheerfully shared the work.

I understood that here there were no longer any servants or masters, men or women: just people who loved, respected and helped each other.

It was both marvelous and new for me!

❖ ❖ ❖

The following day we all went by jeep to Jas des Roberts. In a huge plain, thousands of traders of bric-a-brac displayed an enormous variety of objects.

We found some copper beds, little chests of drawers to store our clothes, a sofa and armchairs where it would be good to relax in front of the fire, and a host of trinkets: place mats, bedspreads, sheets and curtains that would make our home welcoming.

We loaded all this bric-a-brac into the jeep, driven by Arkham, and walked back - it was little more than half a mile.

After lunch, Dagmar said to me:

"We mustn't dawdle, Zahia, you know we have an important appointment."

The barefoot princess

We left together for Plan de la Tour. It was not very far, but the path that led to the kennels seemed everlasting.

We finally arrived. A good hundred or so dogs, both puppies and adults, made a dreadful racket, hoping no doubt to attract our attention.

A little sand-colored Labrador, still unsteady on his feet - he must have been no more than three months old - wagged its tail when it saw me. It was love at first sight for both of us. .

"If you like that one, "said Dagmar, "he's yours, but we'll have to wait a few months before making a ferocious guard dog out of him. He's still a baby, and right now, he's the one who needs you!"

In need of me! Dagmar knew that those words had a special resonance for me. He didn't say them by chance, and my heart overflowed with gratitude and love.

"What name will you give this little fellow, Zahia?"

"I will call him Prince."

The name came to me quite naturally. Dagmar made no comment.

❖ ❖ ❖

In the days that followed we didn't stand idle. In five days the horses would be there and everything had to be ready.

Prince came everywhere with us: he couldn't bear to be left alone in the house. He felt lost, whimpered and got up to mischief: our slippers would not forget it...

The land of the moors

When the great day arrived, the meadow was already turning green and the horse boxes were finished. Arkham and Abdul left together for Nice in the jeep, as one of them would drive the cattle truck on the way back.

The horses got out one by one, and they were magnificent. One of them was a terrible shock for me: he was the spitting image of Medina. He had the same noble bearing, gentle look in his eyes, and mark on his forehead.

"This horse is yours, Zahia," said Dagmar to me, "He's called Khalif, and I know he'll never replace Medina, but I chose him for you, and if he is so much like him, it's because he's Medina's son..."

I could not stop myself from bursting into tears and stammering, between two cascades of weeping,

"That's not possible, master, it's too much!"

A great slap on my behind stopped my moaning at once.

"That's for the "master", Zahia, I warned you that you would be punished!"

And Dagmar let out a wild whoop of laughter, which was so contagious that it shook us all.

The days and months that followed were certainly the happiest of my life. The only black spot was that Arkham and Abdul refused to let me clean out the horse boxes:

"I don't want to upset you, Zahia," Arkham said to me, "But your hands are all calloused, and it would be silly to damage them any more. You are far too pretty for that."

The barefoot princess

I looked at my hands, and saw that Arkham was right, and that evening I treated them with Mamina's balm. After all, I would soon be seventeen, and the time had come to forget the little wild child and become a real woman...

So I devoted my time to helping Dagmar with the servicing and foaling; I also learnt French, as in days gone by I had learnt Arabic and English. I rode and trained the horses, and went on wonderful rides with Khalif, followed everywhere by Prince.

The village of Grimaud was very attractive, with its old houses built on several levels, while the castle was a place where the spirits whispered, and where Mamina welcomed me:

"You are blooming, my child, and it makes me happy, but remember, your path does not stop here. You have a mission to accomplish. The spirits will guide you to someone who will reveal it to you."

"When, Mamina?"

"Soon child, pay attention to the signs!"

"Can't I take a breather for a little while longer, grandma?"

"Certainly you may, Zahia, you still have a few years in front of you here among the people you love and who love you in return, but you will have a task to do which will give you the resources to accomplish your quest, and it won't be easy!"

❖ ❖ ❖

Three months later I was riding Khalif on the beach when I met a little girl in tears.

224

The land of the moors

I dismounted to speak to her:

"Why are you crying, little girl?"

"I've lost my mom, I ran along the beach to look at a fine sand-castle and now I don't know where she is."

I took the child on my saddle and we rode up and down the beach, without success.

Then I noticed the first aid station, where I learnt that the little girl's mother had just left her telephone number.

A lifeguard contacted her and I took her daughter back to her villa, not far from the shore.

Her mother welcomed me warmly, and we got to know each other.

"My name is Vanessa," she told me, "I'm a nurse and my husband is a doctor. We both work for the Red Cross and this house in Gassin is our base. It's where we like to live between humanitarian missions.

Floriane is four and she's already very independent because she is used to running around the savanna and the bush. She finds her way better in those vast open spaces than here, where all the houses look alike."

"No, and that's why they have adopted her. Animals sense those who like them and even the most terrible of predators is nothing compared with some humans who prowl the towns and even the beaches here."

The barefoot princess

"It's difficult to imagine that there is any danger ... there are so many people and everything here seems so... civilized!"

"Don't you believe it, Zahia, only yesterday a young girl was killed on the beach at Grimaud, and that is why I was so afraid for Floriane.

I can't forgive myself for letting my attention wander when she walked off. Thank you so much! I hope we'll see each other again."

❖ ❖ ❖

"The spirits have given me a sign, Mamina, is that young mother the star who will lead me to my destiny?"

"Yes, child, but you must let things take their course..."

227

19

THE QUEEN OF SHEBA

Returning to the farm, I told Leila about my meeting with Floriane and Vanessa, and asked her what the Red Cross was.

"It's a humanitarian association, Zahia, that sends voluntary workers to help people in need. It might be a famine, or after a natural disaster like floods or an earthquake, or war or genocide."

Then I remembered the people who brought us blankets and food after the torrential rains that destroyed our huts and everything we owned. They wore an arm-band with a red cross, and in fact they gave me the only doll I had ever had.

A doctor - perhaps it was Vanessa's husband - had vaccinated us all against the outbreak of cholera which ravaged our region after the floods.

The barefoot princess

"Is the Red Cross the only humanitarian organization, Leila?"

"No, Zahia, there are many others: Frères des hommes, Médecins sans frontières, Bare-foot Doctors..."

"Are all the people who contribute to these missions nurses or doctors?"

"Not always. For instance, Bare-foot Doctors also uses the skills of local shamans and healers.

Dagmar has already helped them, and anybody who sincerely wishes to help is welcome. There is so much misery in this world - and so much indifference!"

I had found my mission, and it only remained to give myself the means to do it, and above all, to wait until I was of age.

❖❖❖

From now on everybody had his own place in our little community. Arkham was very good at looking after the horses, but was not very interested in riding.

Abdul had learnt French quickly, and had a gift for presenting the pure bloods to potential buyers. Word of mouth quickly began to bring results.

As for Leila, her days of reclusion in the harem had left her with a certain taste for solitude. She installed a little office in a comfortable prefabricated chalet, and looked after the accounts, the mail and administrative tasks.

Shoga and Chavha looked after the house and made it their duty to make our lives pleasant and comfortable.

The queen of sheba

To make our stud known Dagmar and I took part in several local events.

The first was the Feast of Horses in Cogolin, where we paraded through the village streets.

Then came an event we had prepared for since we arrived: a beauty contest for horses that would take place in St Tropez, a few miles from Grimaud.

St Tropez is a fishing village whose specialty is to have several faces.

Out of season it is a delicious place with its colored houses and local festivities like the *Bravade*, where the locals recreate the atmosphere of the Napoleonic era, with drums, rifles and costumes.

In season, six months a year, it's the meeting place of theater personalities, well-known painters and rich people who have sumptuous villas there.

Tourists and rubbernecks arrive in droves, hoping to meet their current idols in this illusory paradise.

Parked in camping sites as big as towns, they come to offer themselves a piece of a dream and wait for hours in front of the port hoping to get a glimpse, if only for a moment, of celebrities walking on the decks of their magnificent yachts. It's both marvelous and pathetic.

At the beginning of the twentieth century this village attracted painters and writers, for its light is unique.

The barefoot princess

They were replaced a few decades later by a few cinema and fashion stars, who perpetuated the craze.

This juxtaposition of several worlds, where it is not easy to distinguish reality and illusion, creates a very special atmosphere.

A snare for some, a theater set for others, St Tropez fascinated me because its heterogeneous breeding ground is a powerful magnet for the spirits.

Contrary to what some people think, the spirits hate a vacuum. They need a powerful vibratory fabric to dare to make their voices heard, and clearly this one suits them. Their messages had never been so clear and present for me as here in St Tropez.

Each time I walked through the noisy, perfumed little market with my friends, new revelations assailed me, new images imposed themselves.

Yes, this village has a soul, and perhaps that is what attracts so many people, unconsciously, more than the stars. After all, it is possible to seek the divine in the habit of a monk and silent contemplation, but also in superficial glamour and spangled dresses. Different crucibles, but both reveal the hearts of men.

In any event, in this magic place, a grand feast was in preparation. We had been invited by one of the village's restaurant owners, who had already bought two of our horses.

We chose to present the pearl of our stud: Makeba, a black filly with a white star just in the middle of her forehead. she came from the line of Dagmar's stallion, and my master had decided that I would present this little marvel.

The queen of sheba

"I called this filly Makeba, Zahia, because it was the name of the Queen of Sheba, that Ethiopian who conquered the heart of King Solomon. For me, the Queen of Sheba is you, and so it's logical that you should present her. And for this occasion I have a very special outfit for you."

When I saw the magnificent dress that Leila had designed for me, based on a drawing of the Queen of Sheba, I was both amazed and worried.

"I won't be able to ride with that dress, Dagmar, it's too long and fragile, I'll tear it."

"Yes you will, Zahia, you'll ride Makeba side-saddle, like ladies did in olden days."

"But I don't know how to ride side-saddle".

"I'll teach you, and since you cannot wear a helmet in that outfit, you'll wear a veil: you'll be a sensation, I promise you."

So I concentrated on riding Makeba without stirrups and my legs on one side, covered by my dress, while we executed the haute ecole steps that Dagmar had taught me in Siwa.

When I entered the ring on my filly, I was spontaneously applauded, like in the theater. Dagmar had conceived a floating ballet punctuated by vaulting exercises that impressed both the spectators and the jury.

The barefoot princess

We won the trophy hands down, and I had to submit to a photo session for the local newspapers, which made me the star of the day.

A week after this, a man came to see me at the stud and made me an astonishing proposal.

"I manage a big model agency," he said, "and I was dazzled by your performance and by your beauty. The photos published in the press only confirmed my first impression: you are very photogenic.

I showed the photos to one of my biggest clients and he was very impressed. He heads up a major beauty products corporation and he wants to engage you to be the symbol of his brand."

"I have never posed for photos, and sincerely, I don't know if I could."

"Don't worry about that, Zahia, our photographers have enough experience to make the most of your picture, especially as the photo sessions will take place here, in your own environment. It would be good publicity for your stud and you would receive a large fee for this contract, which is not insignificant."

"Have you spoken about this to Dagmar, who manages this breeding farm, and is effectively my tutor?"

"No, not yet, I wanted to know first if my offer would interest you. I will let you think about it for a couple of days, and I will only settle the formalities with Dagmar when you have given me your answer."

When the man left, I was rather baffled. I thought that it would indeed be a plus for our company, and I also glimpsed a way of being less dependant on Dagmar, and obtaining a sum of money that would allow me to reach my goal. But I was afraid of the reaction of the man who in my secret heart I still called my master.

The queen of sheba

When I explained the project to him, Dagmar said:

"Certainly, it would be a fine piece of advertising for the stud. But what counts more for me is the interest that this experience can bring for you, Zahia.

You are not accustomed to being in the limelight, and if you sign this contract you may commit your future to a path which is not yours."

"Dagmar, I have known my path since the day I met Vanessa, that young woman who works for the Red Cross. I know that I can be useful in aid missions, and apply all the knowledge that Mamina bequeathed me.

But I know that I won't be able to make that commitment before I am 18 and have the resources to be independent. It's a voluntary activity and I have to prove my worth before being accepted by any aid organization. So I must be able to travel and feed myself without having problems."

"I know, my sweet, but don't you realize that when the moment comes I will give you all the financial support you need."

"I know how generous you are, Dagmar, but it's already difficult for me to accept a salary for the work I do here, that brings me so much joy : when I finally spread my wings, there is no question of my still being supported by you."

The barefoot princess

"These scruples do you credit, Zahia, but rest assured that the work you do here is well worthy of the salary I pay you. Just because we enjoy our work doesn't mean we should not be paid a fair price for it.

If I took on a rider as experienced as you, it would cost me much more ... and I would be much less happy.

You mustn't devalue yourself because of your past, my dear. Nevertheless, even if I don't entirely agree, I can understand that you need to assert yourself and give yourself the means to fulfill your dream."

"Does that mean that you are giving me your approval?"

"Yes, Zahia, but as you are not yet of age, I will have to play the role of father to validate the contract, and so I hope you won't disappoint me, but above all, that you won't be disappointed yourself."

"How could I ever deceive you, Dagmar? You know you are everything for me!"

"By not staying yourself, Zahia. By letting yourself be trapped by a world that is only interested in your beauty and not in your soul. I don't want you to lose yourself, that's all!"

"I promise you that."

❖ ❖ ❖

The queen of sheba

The session took place the following week. As well as the photographer and his assistant, there was a hairdresser, a make-up artist and a stylist whose task was to offer me different outfits.

Dagmar - who wanted to be present to keep an eye on things - made the caravan available for all these people, as a changing room.

A variety of clothes were spread over the bed. Straight off, I refused a black leather dress, very short and low-cut, with high boots. I was shocked by the image it gave of a street-girl.

I tried on a sort of turquoise gandura, but I insisted on wearing baggy trousers underneath, because to ride like that, bare-back, would have been uncomfortable as well as indecent.

Several gossamer oriental robes, with several layers of veils, appealed to me but their transparency revealed my figure rather too suggestively for my taste. Nevertheless, I tried them under the pressure of the stylist and the photographer, and I had to admit that the image in the mirror, once I had been made-up and with my hair arranged, overcame my resistance: it was that of the Lady of light.

I rode Makeba side-saddle, veiled, first of all, as for the competition, and then the photographer asked me to take off the veil. His assistant set up big fans, and my loose hair flew as if in a storm. Then I put on the gandura and the baggy trousers. To my displeasure, it was almost transparent, so I could not wear underwear, which would have been as shocking as it would have been unaesthetic.

The barefoot princess

The photographer promised me that once I was moving with Khalif, my horse, I would be in soft focus and my nudity would only be suggested.

Dagmar, Arkham and Abdul were busy with clients, so I accepted, for I would never have dared in their presence.

The results of that first session were conclusive for the client. The photos were superb, though Dagmar thought that some of them were too undressed.

Leila intervened to calm him down, and to remind him that we were in the West, and the values were not the same.

"Zahia is very beautiful, Dagmar, and beauty is never immodest. These photos are artistic: there is no need to blush about them. You who are an aesthete, are you shocked when you look at Botticelli's Venus emerging from the waters in a sea shell?

No, don't worry, darling, your little protégée looks like a princess and the photographer has succeeded in capturing the purity of her soul in her eyes."

The director of the agency, who had come in person to show us the photos, told us:

"My client is about to launch a line of cosmetics for colored women. He is ready to sign a one-year contract and offer a "golden bridge" to Zahia so that she will carry the campaign. There will be photos and also advertising spots for TV and cinemas."

"Will the photos be in the same style as these?" retorted a grumpy Dagmar.

The queen of sheba

"No, it's for beauty products: they'll simply focus on Zahia's face and hair."

The second session took place on a millionaire's yacht at St Tropez and of course I was expected to attend various cocktail parties to whic well-known personalities had been invited.

I was feted, courted and treated like a queen, but that had no effect on me, only the big envelope I received for each of my appearances had any importance for me.

With Leila's benevolent complicity I opened a bank account, where I deposited three quarters of my earnings, while the rest allowed me to spoil those who were dear to me.

I cleaned out the shops with my friends Shoga and Chavha. They weren't difficult to please, for they had been satisfied with so little until then.

I also bought a little prefabricated chalet like Leila's, to set up a real laboratory and books to complete my knowledge of plants and the human body.

I now spoke and read French well enough to nourish my brain and forget the contrived and temporary world in which I had thrown myself, and which was already weighing on me.

I traveled frequently for my photo sessions and got to know splendid cities like Paris and Rome.

Every month I sent money to Adal, because my mother and sisters were illiterate: he was the only person I could communicate with.

The barefoot princess

My brother-in-law now had a phone at home, and although it didn't always function properly, I was able to have news of all the family.

One day, he told me that he and Said were thinking of setting up a farm to grow and export roses.

I offered to help him so that they could set themselves up more quickly; at first he refused, but I was able to convince him that it was for the good of my sisters and their future children : I knew that Mira was expecting a baby.

Adal accepted, on condition that it was just a loan that he would repay me as soon as his company starting making profits. That didn't take long, because the market was expanding rapidly.

When the one-year contract with the cosmetic company expired, I refused categorically to renew it.

I had saved enough money to keep me safe from financial worries for a long time, and in addition I received monthly royalties for the commercials and advertising films I had made.

I would soon be 18, and I wanted to see Vanessa again to talk to her about my projects. She had just returned from a mission in Uganda.

"Zahia," she told me," there has just been serious flooding in Ethiopia. Thousands of people were drowned, and a cholera epidemic is decimating the poor souls who survived. We have very few staff on site, and we would be delighted if you would join us. Of course you would have to prove your worth, but above all your physical and moral fitness for the job."

The queen of sheba

"You are so young, Zahia, could you really face up to all this misery without losing your wonderful exuberance?"

"We don't know each other very well, Vanessa, but let me tell you that young as I am, I have already had to endure terrible trials. Despite them, I survived ... just tell me what I have to do to be part of the team and I'll do it."

"First of all, have your vaccinations against all the diseases that are rife in these distressed countries. You must also have a passport and a visa.

We are leaving a week from now, but if you are unable to complete all the formalities before then, you can come on the next convoy."

When I told Dagmar about this, he called his friend Aghali, attaché at the embassy, to speed up the procedures, and two days before the planned departure, I was able to tell Vanessa that my vaccinations and my papers were in order, and I was ready to go with them.

"There is one thing that bothers me, Zahia, and I have to talk to you about it. You told me that you are Ethiopian, but do you still have family there?"

"Yes, my mother, my sisters and their husbands."

"What will happen if when we arrive in your country, you find that some of your family are among the missing?"

"It would certainly be a terrible trial for me but despite the love I feel for my family, I promise I won't collapse, or give up helping you.

The barefoot princess

"You ought to know, Vanessa, that I am descended from shamans through my grandmother, who is no longer with us.

Wanting to help others is not a teenage whim, but a true calling. Whatever my sorrow or my loss, I will not give up caring for those who suffer: for me it is a sacred duty."

"Prepare your things, Zahia, we leave the day after tomorrow."

❖ ❖ ❖

It was not easy to leave my adopted family, but as always, Dagmar found the true words that appeased my spirit.

"You will return, my child, and you will be even greater and stronger than you are today.

Perhaps you will have great news for us, but don't ask me what: I shan't tell you!

As for your family, you already know what to expect. The day you left your village, you felt that you would never see your mother again.

She wasn't carried away by floods, but by remorse. Prepare yourself for that sad news.

The rest of your family has certainly been very badly hit, but they are alive. You feel it, as I do. Once you are there, who better than you, my dear Zahia, could help them to rebuild their lives?"

The queen of sheba

"Destiny does not strike by chance, and your quest is taking you back to Ethiopia because it is a necessary step for you."

"Thank you, Master: and please don't punish me this time, because it is not the little slave girl who is speaking, but the woman whom you revealed to herself and for whom you will always be her roots, and her master-tree."

Destiny is simply the accelerated force of time

Jean Giraudoux

20

THE FORCE OF DESTINY

The flight in the military plane was very tiring. We ran into a huge storm that shook us badly and made me ill. I was rather ashamed, despite Vanessa's kindness. She told me she had felt the same, the first time.

When finally we arrived in the province of Gondar, the sky was still heavy with unexpressed threats. We just had time to land between two tropical downpours.

"Put on these rubber boots before disembarking, Zahia, the ground is soaked, and you'll get stuck and lose your shoes."

The disaster was so massive that I hardly recognized my country. Torrents of mud had swept down the mountain slopes, taking with them huts and whole herds of sheep and goats, whose horns emerged here and there from the moving magma. I hardly dared think that under that silt-laden mass lay human beings who had not had the time or the means to flee.

The barefoot princess

The town, once so welcoming, had lost its trees and roofs, torn away by the storms. The shops were closed, and access to them was impossible. It was like a huge, vast cemetery.

"We'll have to wait for the helicopter," said Vanessa, "It's the only way to reach the reception center, near Mekele."

I quivered. I had not told her the name of my home village, but when she saw my distress she understood.

"It's going to be a difficult trial for you, Zahia; I hope that you will stand the shock".

When we flew over my village, it was deserted, abandoned. How could I obtain news of my family?

"Don't worry," said the pilot, "We evacuated the survivors to Addis Ababa: the capital was spared from the floods."

That still didn't reassure me, but I had the contact details for Radia and Aghali and I knew that if I got in touch with them, they would do everything possible to get news for me.

When we reached the bush hospital, sited on a high point, there were so many poor people to treat that I no longer had time to think about my family.

I had brought my medicine bag that never left me, but it wasn't enough, and I also had a case containing all the medications I had prepared before leaving.

Offered a rest, I refused: I had to begin work immediately, or I would have gone mad.

The force of destiny

The first face I saw after putting on my sterile clothing was that of Selma, the healer. She moved busily from one bed to another, and I was pleased to see that she was making full use of Mamina's precious exercise book.

"Hello, Zahia," she said, "They told me you were coming. We're going to do good work together." She hesitated a little before continuing:

"I know you have the gift of divination, so I can't lie to you. Your dear mother left us a month ago. I tried everything to save her, but she no longer wanted to live. She passed away quietly, without suffering, like a candle that has been blown out."

"Thank you, Selma, I knew that my last visit was like a goodbye."

"Her last words were for you, 'If you see Zahia, ask her to forgive me.' ...."

"I forgave her a long time ago, Selma. Now let's get on with the work. My mother had her God but these people only have us."

The weeks which followed were a real nightmare, but together we all managed to save lives, and my herbs worked miracles to relieve the suffering.

"Your presence and your medications are indispensable, Zahia," Vanessa's husband told me, "We are badly short of drugs. We have no more morphine or antibiotics. We're waiting for a plane to deliver some to us, but the pilot must be caught in a storm: he is usually very punctual. Pray heaven he arrives in time!"

"Anyway, I'm going to prepare a list of what we need urgently, because what we ordered won't be enough. He'll have to make a second trip."

I tried several times to phone Addis Ababa, but the lines were down, and the electricity was cut as well.

We operated with a power generator but it was not powerful enough to light us all the time, so we used oil lamps, and switched on the generator only for emergencies; mainly amputations.

Then the expected plane landed, on what was more like an ice-rink than a landing strip, and Vanessa, who was assisting her husband during a delicate operation, asked me to go and collect the precious parcels and give the messenger the list of medications for the next delivery.

When I reached him, the pilot was occupied with freeing the propeller from a mass of herbs and mud. Then he turned to face me, and I was rooted to the spot: the man in front of me was Prince Selim.

"Don't just stand there, Zahia, these drugs are urgent. There isn't a minute to lose. Don't you have a list to give me?"

I was dumfounded by his coolness. He hadn't moved a muscle when he saw me. Still in shock, I gave him the list without saying a word.

"Have you lost your voice again? That would be a pity, because I'm not leaving until tomorrow morning and I have every intention of asking you to explain yourself. I have all night!"

The force of destiny

I ran away, not forgetting the urgency of my mission. The poor man on the operating table was in serious need of antibiotics if he was not to die from septicemia.

Yet, selfishly, what tormented me was how to escape from the Prince? I could hardly lock myself in the washrooms until he left.

"You're trembling, Zahia, you look as though you've seen a ghost!" Vanessa said to me.

She didn't know how true that was!

❖ ❖ ❖

When we had finished treating the patients, and I made it last as long as possible, I could see that Selim was watching me: he had no intention of letting me go.

"You are very busy, Zahia, and very competent too, but don't overdo it because I too have wounds that need treating."

After dinner, Selim took me by the arm and led me aside, into a corner of the room.

"Why did you run away, Zahia? That question has been haunting me for years. Did I mistreat you? Did I force myself on you? Tell me, I need to know ..."

"Highness ..."

"No!" he interrupted bluntly, "Here I am Selim, nobody else. No-one knows my true identity, though I've worked for aid organizations for years. I am simply the pilot of a little bush plane who delivers drugs to the most outlying parts of the world, and that is how I wish to be known."

"Well, Selim, I acknowledge that you treated me kindly and with respect, even though I was only a prisoner, dependent on your goodwill..."

"You were a slave, Zahia, and although I bought you, I never treated you as a captive."

"I was torn from my family when I was eleven years old and sold as a slave to the masters of Siwa. But I found a generous man in Dagmar, who was able to dress my wounds and become my master, in the noblest sense of the word.

He taught me everything about the art of horses and thanks to him I found peace in my heart.

Your ... interest ... that I aroused despite myself, uprooted me once again, but that is not why I fled."

"Why then, Zahia?"

"For Leila and her family".

"Leila was a leper, and when I learnt of her terrible disease, instead of abandoning her in a leper colony I kept her with me, and I gave her all I could to relieve her suffering."

"Why didn't you have her examined by a competent doctor, Selim?"

The force of destiny

"Because she didn't wish it."

"Did you ever ask her why?"

"Leila told me that she didn't want to be treated in a hospital but that her only consolation was to live and die near to her son, Arkham, who I always treated like my own child."

"Sorry, Selim, but you are completely wrong. What Leila didn't want was to suffer your attentions, and that disease arrives at the right moment to protect her."

"Am I so repulsive, Zahia, that a woman would prefer to be a leper than to become my wife?"

"Leila was simply the wife of another man, and whether he was dead or alive, she did not wish to betray him.

I happened to become her friend, and I was able to see that her disease was not leprosy but a simple skin disease: contagious, but perfectly commonplace.

At first she refused to use my balm, though she knew it could heal her, but in talking to her I learnt that she was the wife of Dagmar, the master of the horse at Siwa who had been mourning her for years.

After that revelation it only took a few days for her to accept my treatment, and be cured. So then we conceived our escape plan."

"Yes, I know: Arkham stole my jeep. I found it with the fisherman who helped your escape."

"He didn't steal it, Selim, he just borrowed it. He is a man of honor. In my bag I have an envelope with the sum it was worth. Arkham asked me to give it to you if by chance I saw you again one day. I think that's now done ..."

"That's not necessary, Zahia, I have my jeep back, and anyway that is not why I am bitter. I mention it only in disappointment. I brought that young man up and loved him like my own son. His escape hurt me deeply."

"He had to choose between his mother, his father, and you, Selim. But he hesitated a long time, and not a day goes by when he doesn't speak of you."

"And where does Shoga come in to all this?"

"Shoga and Arkham love each other - and they are going to get married. They met when she brought him the mail to be posted. She acted as the go-between."

"Where are they now, Zahia?"

"I'll tell you if you promise not to cause them any problems: I trust your word."

"I promise you."

"They are all in France where Dagmar bought a stud farm. I took part in that great adventure myself, before I came of age, because my true calling is to care for those who suffer, as my grandmother, who was a shaman, taught me.

This is my first mission, and it is all the more trying because I have just learnt that my mother, who lived near Mekele, is dead, and I have no news of my sisters and their husbands."

The force of destiny

"They may have been evacuated to Addis Ababa, but the telephone lines are down and I can't reach Dagmar's friends, who could get news for me."

"I can help you, because that is where I am going tomorrow, to collect the drugs you need. When I return, I will have news for you."

"Thank you so much, Selim. Are you still angry?"

"I'm not angry, Zahia. I was never angry with you. I just didn't understand why you ran away, and it affected me deeply. You seemed so happy....

And do you remember that evening when we rode together in the desert? I don't think we were so indifferent to each other then. That evening, I must admit, you were so pretty that I had to control myself to respect the promise I had made to Dagmar."

"It's true that I was affected by your presence, Selim, I can't deny it, but I was very young, and I did what I had to do: I couldn't delay reuniting those people who had suffered so much. Now they are my true family, and I regret nothing."

"But *I* do, Zahia, because if you had stayed, you would certainly have become my wife."

"That seems impossible, even to think about, Selim: we are far too different.

I'm a wild child, brought up in the savanna. I talk to spirits. I break all the taboos of your religion by riding horses disguised as a man. And above all, I'm a free woman, intractable, and I demand to be treated as an equal by the man I love.

The barefoot princess

Do you think that would have been compatible with a harem, veiled women, and especially with your mother who regiments the whole palace?"

"My mother is dead, Zahia, and I don't have a harem any longer."

"And what have you done with your wives?"

"They were never my wives, and even less my concubines, even if some of them had that hope deep in their hearts.

I have never been attracted to submissive women, and the few relationships I was able to have were with western women during my studies in France or during my travels.

Leila was the only exception, because she was beautiful and cultivated. I certainly intended to make her my wife, despite the age difference.

The women of my harem - or rather of my father's harem, for all I did was to perpetrate his memory and customs - have been married to men who can make them happy. Only two have remained in my service. They have become my nursing aids."

"Why, Selim, are you ill?"

"No, Zahia, I have turned the rooms and apartments of the harem into a health center for the needy. I only kept the private apartments for myself."

The force of destiny

"Are you really telling me the truth?"

"Yes, and my only regret is not to have a little Zahia by my side, to share my life and my passions."

"Excuse me, Prince, but I'm tired. All you have said touches me truly, but I need time to see clearly how my heart feels. If you wish, we could take up this conversation again when you return."

"Is that a complete refusal, Zahia, is your heart already committed elsewhere? It wouldn't be surprising, you are so lovely!"

"No Selim, there is nobody in my life. No man has so far succeeded in making my heart beat. It's just that I have spent twelve hours giving all my energy to people who suffer, and I need a rest."

"Then I'll not say "adieu" but "au revoir", Zahia!"

I took his "au revoir" to mean that he looked forward to seeing me again. I smiled at him: he understood that we were on the same wavelength...

❖ ❖ ❖

Three days later, Selim returned to the camp with the drugs, and also with very good news of my sisters and their husbands.

"I saw them in the hospital in Addis Ababa, Zahia. They have lost everything but they are in good health, which is the main thing, isn't it? I promised them that I would take you with me on the next trip.

The barefoot princess

I also gave them some funds, so they wouldn't be completely penniless".

"Tell me what you gave them, Selim. I'll repay you at once."

"Don't be an idiot, Zahia, I would have done it for any person in need. I already regret telling you about it."

"But Selim, I'm rich - not as rich as you, of course, but before leaving I worked as model and it's up to me to meet my family's needs."

"Don't be so proud, young lady! Don't you realize that you only have to say the word, for all that I own to be yours? What would you say if I asked you to marry me?"

"I would say that it was a little rushed, Selim. I admit that I like you, and you attract me more than any other man has done. But is that enough for me to marry you?

What you said the other evening proved to me that you are sincere and generous, but if I committed myself to you for life ... it would be the end of my calling, and I do not want that!"

"Why do you think I would expect you to make such a sacrifice? In this field I have more experience than you, even if I don't have your gift. There is nothing to stop us teaming up. What do you think?"

"I've told you, Selim, I have my requirements: I don't want to pledge allegiance, nor have any constraints. Could you put up with such a rebellious wife?"

The force of destiny

"Of course, Zahia, I want you as you are. As I love you, and have loved you since the very first day, when you were only a young boy who affected me strangely, despite myself.

But do you think you could love *me* one day?"

"I already love you, Selim, and I think I love you since that evening ride at Jahal."

"Then don't resist any more, my sweet, or you will make us both unhappy."

"All this is so fast, Selim ... and I am so inexperienced."

"Be silent, darling. Come into my arms, that is where you should be. And don't tell me you don't want to, I can see the desire in your eyes. Let me kiss you: I've been waiting for this first kiss for such a long time."

"Before it is too late, my love, I have to tell you something ... and it's terribly embarrassing!"

"What's that, my sweet?"

"I'm ... whole. My grandmother wouldn't let me be excised. And also, I'm not ... smooth, despite the insistence of your servant girls in the harem. Is that bad for you? Will you reject me?"

"On the contrary, it's marvelous, little girl. At last I'm going to hold a real woman in my arms," said Selim, holding me very tight.

You were right, Dagmar, I have great news for you: I love and am loved. And this time, I can feel that it's for life.

EPILOGUE

"Mamina, Mamina!"

"Yes, Lila, what do you want me for?"

"Where did you find that pretty shell that you always wear around your neck?"

"My grandmother bequeathed it to me, child, when I was about your age."

"Mamina, will you give it to me too?"

"Yes Lila, but only when I feel the spirits calling me."

"Well then I hope it will be as late as possible, Mamina, because I love you and I don't want to lose you."

"You will never lose me, my child; I will always live, as long as you keep me in your heart."

I feel a hand on my round stomach, the hand of Selim, my beloved husband.

The barefoot princess

"On the contrary, darling, my dearest wish is to hold a little Zahia in my arms. Will she have your gifts, my sweet?"

"No, it's her daughter who will take up the torch. Her name will be Lila."

"You were dreaming, Zahia, you spoke aloud. Do you feel well, my love?"

"Yes, Selim, and I hope you won't be disappointed, it's a girl!"

Printed December 2008
by Nouvelle Imprimerie Laballery - 58500 Clamecy
Legal deposit : March 2008   Print number 812200

Printed in France

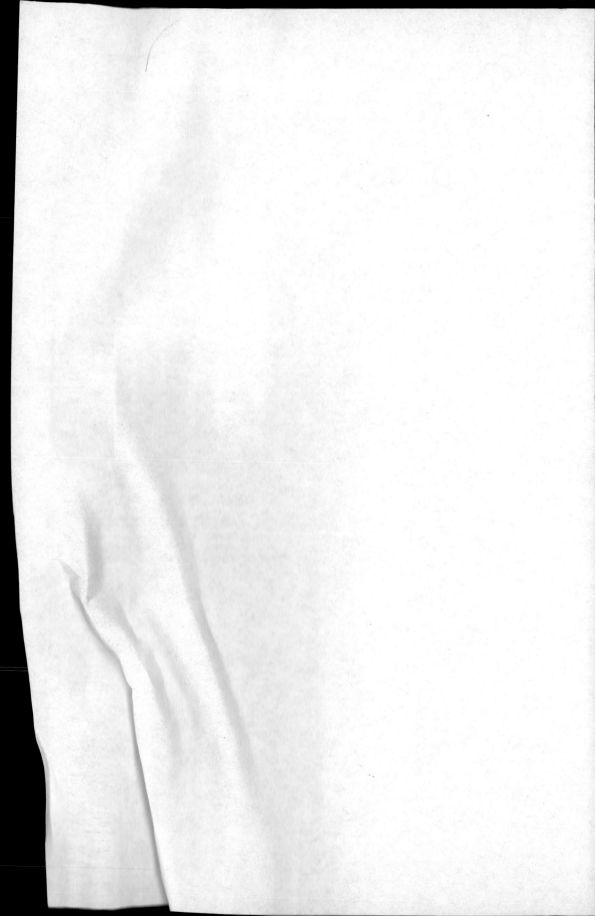